SKELETON CLOCKS

SKELETON CLOCKS

F. B. ROYER-COLLARD
F.B.H.I.

N.A.G. PRESS LTD, LONDON, EC1V 7QA

First edition 1969
Enlarged edition 1977
Reprinted 1981

ISBN 7198 0110 9

© F. B. Royer-Collard and
N.A.G. Press Ltd., London, England, 1969 and 1977

Printed and bound in Great Britain by
Morrison & Gibb Ltd., London and Edinburgh

CONTENTS

INTRODUCTION *1*

1 DEVELOPMENT OF THE ENGLISH SKELETON CLOCK *3*

2 SOME ENGLISH SKELETON CLOCKS *23*

3 ENGLISH SKELETON CLOCK MANUFACTURERS *37*

4 DEVELOPMENT OF THE FRENCH SKELETON CLOCK *64*

5 SOME FRENCH SKELETON CLOCKS *73*

6 COMPLEX SKELETON CLOCKS *93*

7 YEAR CLOCKS, LONGCASE, AND MUSICAL CLOCKS *109*

8 AUSTRIAN, AMERICAN AND NOVELTY CLOCKS *126*

9 SKELETON CLOCKS IN BUCKINGHAM PALACE *136*

10 MORE SKELETON CLOCKS FROM PAST AND PRESENT *141*

11 SKELETON CLOCKS AT THE GREAT EXHIBITION *157*

12 SHADES: CLOCK REPAIR *162*

GLOSSARY *167*

INDEX *168*

INTRODUCTION

On a November night in the year 1911, I had just been initiated in the art of 'putting up the shutter'. This assignment was to be with me for many months to come. It had been a red letter day because it was my first as a clockmaker's apprentice.

I was somewhat bewildered by all the clock mechanisms that surrounded me. A great number of skeleton clocks were in this workshop and on the shelves, and their intriguing visible movements fascinated me as much then as they do now.

In general, horologists have always treated them as insignificant and just a passing phase, as if they were ashamed of them, and considered them unworthy even of mention. Moreover inventors, designers, and manufacturers of skeleton clocks seemed to have effaced themselves as if they had created a monster!

No textbook provides much information about the unnamed tens of thousands of skeleton clocks. Despite the wealth of detail and variety, the subject has been left untapped until now. The retort I make when asked 'Why write about skeleton clocks?' is that I have always known there were great potentialities to be explored in this field.

I wrote a short article exclusively on the skeleton clock in the *Horological Journal* of December 1962, and subsequently a reprint appeared in the *Bulletin* of the National Association of Watch and Clock Collectors Inc., of U.S.A. It was received in America with tremendous interest and enthusiasm because many thousands of these clocks have found their way there.

As the first horologist to go into this endless and exhilarating topic I was pressed by many friends and horological enthusiasts, as well as owners who gave me access to their collections, to write a book that would be informative, not too complicated, and profusely illustrated, as a record of the much maligned skeleton clock.

This is the result. I have specifically refrained from describing in any detail the various escapements utilised in any skeleton formula. These technicalities have been written and re-written with diagrams and illustrations in so many previous books, and aired with such competence, that any contribution of mine would be futile. The publishers, however, thought a simple glossary would help non-horological readers, and this was kindly provided for me by Eric Bruton, Esq.

Although the following chapters will demonstrate the evolution of the skeleton clock more or less chronologically, there are many deviations in order to give emphasis to an item of importance.

To assist in the recognition of manufacturers and styles, I have purposely included items which may seem frivolous, but they are the ingredients that gave individuality to these clocks.

In diagnosing the development of the skeleton clock, it was found best to treat the English approach to manufacture separately from that of the Continent. Each nation differs fundamentally in its approach and the general form of the clock was originated on the Continent. In chapters two and five dealing with individual English and French skeleton clocks, I have endeavoured to show a collection of clocks as comprehensive as possible which will enable the reader to distinguish the salient features in each type.

Being the first publication on the subject, this book obviously cannot include the entire range of clocks. There may be in existence many others that I have not seen. That so many wonderful and superb specimens can be illustrated, is mainly due to the kindness and generosity of individuals who have given me unstinted information and access to their collections, or individual possessions.

In correspondence from all over the world were suggestions that a list of skeleton clockmakers should be included for reference and, as a result, many names were submitted to me. After careful consideration, I have decided that it would only be perpetuating inaccuracies to publish such a list.

The majority of names on skeleton clocks, often engraved on escutcheons, cartouches, plaques, brass strips, and other media, were added by the retailers of the day. The makers did not intend to send out their newly made products with such plates, screwed on, riveted indiscriminately and often incongruously to the frame.

The name on the clock is often the retailer's and he was only very rarely also the maker of the clock. Stringent and exhaustive enquiries of archaeological and historical societies, libraries, and local research groups, have proved these findings beyond all shadow of doubt.

A curious fact is that some whose names appear on skeleton clocks were even without proper accommodation, let alone facilities for making clock mechanisms in any quantity. What is of great significance, however, is the evidence that they were not even sufficiently important for their memories to be perpetuated.

It is a consoling thought that, in this second half of the twentieth century, skeleton clocks have regained some of their popularity. Today's antique boutiques, together with the antique markets, are placing a more worthy price on them. The salerooms, following suit, must now give encouragement to their many owners by making them aware that their clocks are becoming a status symbol. Glass shades are to be had at a premium, and the 'backroom boys' are trekking the land to unearth these forgotten treasures. Could this mean the rebirth of the forgotten industries of skeleton clocks and glass shades?

Few imagined that in the 1960s the French carriage clock would make such a strong come-back. We may yet see the resurrection of the skeleton clock in all its glory, accompanied by the statuettes, waxed fruits, imitation flowers, and stuffed birds of the Victorian era.

F. B. Royer-Collard

12 Beaconsfield Road,
Hastings, Sussex.

ACKNOWLEDGEMENTS

To H.M. the Queen for her gracious permission to have photographed the two William Congreve skeleton clocks in her private apartments at Buckingham Palace and, for granting reproduction of them, with the drawing taken from the pictorial inventory.

To Geoffrey de Bellaigue Esq., The Deputy Surveyor of the Queens' Works of Art, at St. James's Palace, who gave such valued co-operation and assistance, and to Frank L. Thirkell, Esq., of Charles Frodsham & Co. Ltd., the Queen's Clockmakers, who arranged for the removal of the dial from the Congreve extreme detached escapement clock, for photography.

To The Trustees of the British Museum for allowing photography of the Le Roy One-wheel Clock, and the Berthoud Year Clock, also to the British Museum, P. G. Coole, Esq., and B. Hutchinson, Esq., for helpful answers to my queries.

To the Directors of the Museum, Conservatoire National Des Arts and Metiers, Paris, for permission to reproduce their three mantel skeleton clocks.

To the Director, The City of Liverpool Museum, for kindly allowing me to portray the photographs of their Condliff skeleton clock, and to Alan Smith, Esq., Keeper of Ceramics and Applied Art, for all his efforts on my behalf.

To the Director of the Birmingham Museum for permission to reproduce the photograph of the Scott's Memorial skeleton clock by Evans.

To the Director of the Royal Scottish Museum, Edinburgh, for granting me leave to reproduce photographs of their musical skeleton clock.

To The Astronomer Royal for supplying such interesting data on the Greenwich Time signal system.

To Monsieur A. Lengelle for kindly giving me permission to reproduce the photograph of the French wheel skeleton clock in *La Pendule Française*, by Tardy.

To the British Horological Institute for their valuable assistance on several occasions.

To the Town Halls, and the many libraries up and down the country who were painstaking in their answers to my many requests, especially the Hastings Municipal Library and their co-operative staff.

To the various archaeological, historical, and local research societies particularly Mrs. F. C. Robson of the Belper Historical Society, and G. C. H. Le Cocq, Esq., of Societe Jersiaise, Jersey, and the Stourbridge Historical Society.

To the *Liverpool Daily Post*, *The Jersey Weekly*, *The Holmfirth Express*, *Antiquarian Horology*, *Retail Jeweller* and *The Bulletin*, *N.A.W.C.A.*, U.S.A., for their generous publicity, and for the *Daily Mail*'s permission to use the illustration of the Coldwell skeleton clock taken from the *News Chronicle*, Leeds edition.

To Major Anthony Heathcote, Norman Langmaid, Esq., U.S.A., S. P. Lehv, Esq., M.D., U.S.A., Albert L. Odmark, Esq., U.S.A., with sincere thanks to them for permitting me to have access to their extensive collection of skeleton clocks for photography and publication.

To Miss P. B. Evans, of Handsworth Wood, Birmingham, and to Mrs. S. Cooper, of Hambleton, for the interesting anecdotes and photographs of their ancestors.

To C. W. Haycock, Esq., of Ashbourne, for the photographs, drawings, and anecdotes of the family business.

To Sir Hugh Chance for the story and information in the making of the glass shades, etc., and in the same connection to Messrs. Pilkington Bros., of St. Helens.

To Harry Birnbaum, Esq., of New York, for permitting me to examine, and photograph the skeleton clock section of the John Smith & Sons catalogue dated 1865, in his possession.

To Miss Hazel Victoria Bryan for her advice and collaboration.

To my friend Eric Bruton, Esq., for his untiring efforts on my behalf with both advice and photography.

To Charles Allix, Esq., the well-known horological bookseller, for sparing some of his precious time in reading the manuscript and also for the photographs from his own collection of skeleton clocks.

Finally, my grateful thanks and appreciation to all the above, and many more, too numerous to mention, who have contributed in one way and another, not forgetting an avid enthusiast, Charles C. Mellor, Esq., of Greensburgh, U.S.A., the owner of one single modest skeleton clock who terms it his 'one pride and joy'.

1-1 *A Gothic clock of skeleton form, but not regarded as a skeleton clock*

CHAPTER 1

THE DEVELOPMENT OF THE ENGLISH SKELETON CLOCK

'Seeing is believing' probably may be the best reason for displaying the working mechanism of a clock. It was during the Industrial Revolution, when people were becoming more aware of machinery, that the skeleton clock became popular.

At the beginning of the sixteenth century, many early Gothic domestic clocks were made with iron frames in skeleton design. The upper structure, as shown in Fig. 1-1, is certainly a skeleton and not unlike many clocks produced some three hundred years later. However, Gothic iron clocks are not being included in this book, which deals only with the latter half of the eighteenth century, the nineteenth century and the early years of the twentieth century.

It is generally accepted that skeleton clocks were confined to the Victorian era, in particular the latter half of the nineteenth century, when they were made in great numbers by English manufacturers. This is not the fact.

There is overwhelming evidence that the skeleton clock was first produced in its recognised form from about 1752 onwards by celebrated French masters such as Lepaute, Pierre Le Roy, Lepine, Berthoud and a host of others, who succeeded, by a combination of mathematics and simple design, in reducing a train of wheels from three to two, or even one.

The skeleton clock mechanism, with its plates cut away to show the train, is an interesting example of eighteenth, nineteenth, and early twentieth century workmanship and taste, though it contributed nothing to the art of time-keeping.

Both seventeenth and eighteenth century English longcase and bracket clocks are often described as having 'skeleton dials' because, in these clocks, the chapter ring is pierced or fretted out. The dictionary, however, defines 'skeleton' as 'the general supporting framework of anything'. It can thus have a very wide interpretation.

It has been suggested that English skeleton clocks were one-of-a-kind thesis pieces made by graduate apprentices. I can find no shred of evidence to substantiate this theory.

For nearly two hundred and fifty years English manufacturers shrouded their clock movements in wooden, or, on occasions, metal cases, both with some decoration added. The engraved backplate, the decorative engraved apron on the pallet cock and, indeed, the whole mechanism, was completely boxed in and never seen. Cases became relatively stereotyped.

Continental clockmakers, particularly the French, concentrated on artistic development of cases and employed only the finest artists and sculptors in their manufacture. Always flamboyant, French cases became more so and have, indeed, remained so ever since.

The English eighteenth-century clock, unlike the Continental, was the result of a tremendous commercial undertaking and a united effort by manufacturers took place which tended to create an aura around their designs.

It was in this atmosphere that the English skeleton clock was born and came into its own in the nineteenth century, following in the wake of

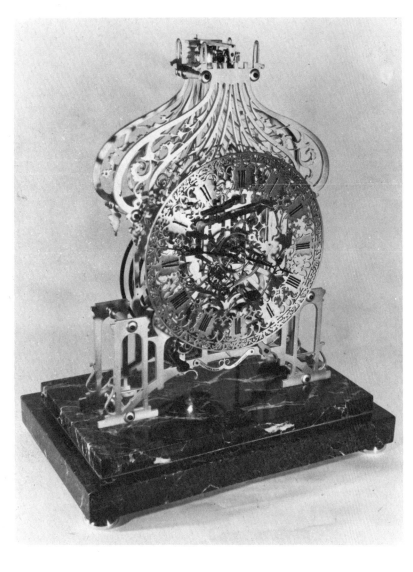

allow such markings. The ban would, of course, include any other embellishments which might enable one to recognise a clock's maker or origin.

Even when a skeleton clock does bear a maker's name, the name is very difficult to corroborate. Extensive research has failed to find a concrete solution to this problem. Enemy action played a considerable part in the destruction of valuable records. The few makers that remained, left the clockmaking industry – which declined to its lowest ebb in the 1930s – and the rest were absorbed into other and more profitable ventures.

In spite of these obstacles, enough conclusive evidence has survived to show that a mere handful of manufacturers was occupied with this form of production. Many of the names submitted for identification are those of clock owners and not the makers. The practice of labelling a clock with its owner's name was possibly to give the air of possession that the Americans call 'personalising'.

Types of clock

It is best to use the word 'frame' rather than 'plate' for all skeleton clocks, because it describes this component more precisely.

There are approximately three types of frame, whatever their origin. These are:

(1) *fretted*,
(2) *scroll*, and
(3) the simple geometrical bar, or *rafter*, design.

Throughout this book the last type will be termed, for convenience, 'rafter'.

Many different names, such as 'fret clocks', 'hobbies clocks', 'visible clocks' and, an American expression 'cut-out clocks', have been used for what is generally accepted as the skeleton clock. The word 'visible' is used also for clocks where some part of the mechanism is perceivable to the eye or open to observation.

Hundreds of thousands of French clocks with drab and monumental-looking cases are described as having a 'visible escapement'. This escapement is the Brocot – an eye-catcher when one enters a room – with frost gilt escape wheel, pallet arms, and cock, showing red pins or pallets, made of cornelian or agate. Whether or not these clocks, which were produced in the mid-half of the nineteenth century, were a competitive answer to British skeleton clocks can only be surmised.

The Americans were not slow to pick up the threads from the French and produced cast iron clock cases housing the same form of escapement which, in American terminology, became known as an 'outside escapement'.

These clocks cannot legitimately be called skeleton clocks although that name is bestowed on them in many of the best saleroom catalogues.

French clocks of the same type which already had the advantage of seventy years' success.

Another fallacy accepted by the public is that only *four* skeleton clocks were ever made, and those only for the Great Exhibition of 1851. The considerable numbers of these clocks one sees bear witness to the prodigious output of the Victorian years.

Very few skeleton clocks bear the names of their makers, trade marks, numbers or other means of identification. Perhaps this absence of mark was peculiar to the kind of clock. I have it on good authority, substantiated by a manufacturer whose forebears made skeleton clocks, that the business houses, particularly those in London, would in no circumstances

1-3 *Fretted design representing a cathedral with 8-bell chime*

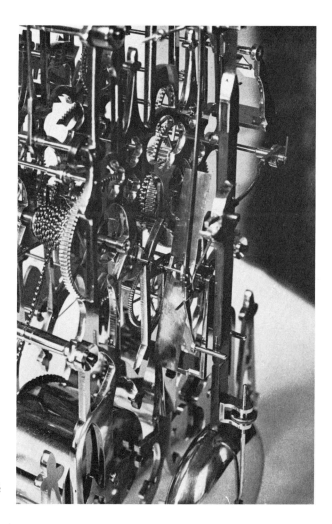

1-4 *Back of a clock, with a rare gravity escapement*

A true skeleton clock has both frames extensively cut out, or a frame showing the whole of the movement with its going and striking mechanisms from any angle, whilst the visible clock has only the dial plate removed, exposing the striking working parts and the motion work.

The English skeleton clock dates roughly from 1820 and gave a new lease of life to the clock industry for the next seventy or eighty years. Skeleton clock output was huge and ran into tens of thousands.

The English skeleton clock is easily recognised and, in most cases, is of a fretted design. This term must not be confused with the frets which are included in the design of wooden cases found in seventeenth- and eighteenth-century clocks.

Although the English skeleton clock is of a heavy appearance, there was a sturdiness and solidarity about it which showed the thoroughness of its maker. It was generally regarded then, as now, as a fine piece of engineering. Occasionally planted in the bases of English clocks was the odd gilt or ormolu figure, which looks incongruous.

The marble fireplaces of our Victorian grandparents, being of gargantuan proportions, not only carried the weight of these massive clocks, but supported the lofty mirrors which so admirably reflected the skeleton frame and its working mechanism.

The clocks were produced by manufacturers, mainly from London, Birmingham, Liverpool, Derby, and Prescot. A handful also emerged in Wakefield, Leeds, and Sheffield. A number of skeleton clocks – complicated and otherwise – are attributed to individuals in other small towns, but there appears to be no real evidence to authenticate them. Only a microscopic percentage of the makers of clocks designed to individual specifications can be accounted for.

The majority of skeleton clocks were made to go for eight days but a

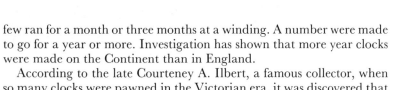

1-5 *Scroll design of an individually-designed clock with its mercury pendulum*

An example of a cathedral clock with an eight-bell peal, quarter chiming mechanism, is shown in Fig. 1-3. Even the Great Wheel at the Earls Court Exhibition of 1880 gave the designers inspiration.

Another vogue was for the reproduction of famous public buildings or monuments. One such clock was formed to represent the Scott Memorial in Edinburgh as shown in Fig. 3-2. This was manufactured solely in Birmingham. Many unusual escapements and other technical features were incorporated, such as the gravity escapement in Fig. 1-4.

From its beginning in the early nineteenth century, the tempo of skeleton clock production in this country increased year by year, until saturation point seemed to have been reached, when it slowed down almost to a halt in the twentieth century.

There was nothing revolutionary in setting out of the trains of gears to accommodate this new trend. Each train was laid out on the drawing board and conventionally positioned relative to each other, but their actual placing within the skeleton frame was arranged to satisfy the demands of the particular frame design.

few ran for a month or three months at a winding. A number were made to go for a year or more. Investigation has shown that more year clocks were made on the Continent than in England.

According to the late Courteney A. Ilbert, a famous collector, when so many clocks were pawned in the Victorian era, it was discovered that skeleton clocks were particularly acceptable to pawnbrokers and one firm went as far as to manufacture from scratch, skeleton clocks which were intended to be pawned.

To be able to show the mechanisms working and to offer the public exotic shapes in brass, gave a new impetus to makers. Innumerable frame designs were created and included wheatsheaves, lyres, heart-shapes, circles, architectural features, and Gothic cathedrals, geometrical fantasies such as Westminster Abbey, Milan Cathedral, York Minster, and the Royal Pavilion, Brighton (Figs. 1-2 and 2-25) taking pride of place.

1-6 *Early English scroll design*

Once the patterns were decided upon, the frames were cast and hand finished. There were exceptions where a purchaser would commission an unusual or personal design. This would have necessitated the piercing of the frame by hand, which was a costly project in comparison with batch production techniques.

A typical example of individual design is that owned by Mrs. Lee Guinness, who is connected with the family so famous in the brewing industry. This clock, shown in Fig. 1-5, was commissioned in lieu of an outstanding debt and is one of the largest and heaviest skeleton clocks known. It was made in London to special order in 1880.

The frames are three-tenths of an inch thick and have massive pillars. The clock has a dead beat escapement and the train is equally robust and magnificently made with regulator type six-arm crossings or spokes on each wheel. There is beat adjustment and – unusual for a skeleton clock – it has a mercurial pendulum. The frame has a scroll design, the terminals ending in ivy leaves. The movement is mounted on a white marble base and it takes two people to lift the clock.

It is extremely rare to see an English skeleton clock movement with a going barrel. All trains are normally driven through a fusee. On the occasions where barrel work is encountered it is always of a much later date. This was an encroachment by German makers on quality for the sake of cheapness and in, incidentally, low calibre brass.

The English skeleton clock covered every aspect of clock mechanism from a simple timepiece, by way of 'one-stroke-at-the-hour', ordinary strike, quarter strike on two bells, ting tang, four bell quarters to eight bell and sixteen bell musical chimes.

Wire steel gongs took the place of bells in later years, although some bell movements continued. The few longcase clocks that were made incorporated Harrington patent carrillon tubes.

The 1890s brought with them the decline and fall of the skeleton clock.

Features of English clocks

Once the trains had been planted, movements were not confined or restricted to case measurements. Therefore the size of the train, whether timepiece, strike, chimes or musical, presented no problem. Ordinary timepieces were produced on a larger scale than striking or chiming mechanisms at an estimated ratio of eight to one in favour of the timepiece.

An early striking skeleton clock in heart-shape frame, with the rear frame pinned, not screwed, and with a cocked fly or fan, can be seen in Fig. 1-6. Here the mainsprings can be seen through the fretted barrel caps (a legacy from the French). A rare feature on the earlier English skeleton clock was that the ratchet work was set up on the rear frame.

Rack mechanisms for both hour and quarters sequences prevailed in all English skeleton clocks, no count wheel or locking plate being employed. A form of count wheel or locking plate, however, is used in musical skeleton clocks. These normally have just one slot or notch which enables the cylinder or chiming barrel to complete one turn in its cycle before being locked.

The simplest and most popular form of strike can be seen in Fig. 1-7, and first took shape in the 'one-at-the-hour' strike – a term by which it is commonly known. A lifting piece or hammer tail is fitted to the square of

1-7 *'One-at-the-hour' strike*

1-8 *Platform lever escapement of a Lichfield cathedral clock*

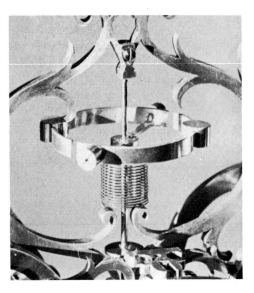

1-9 *Chronometer style balance wheel and spring*

the extended hammer arbor, the pin fixed to the minute wheel (or, in earlier versions, a snail), lifts the hammer and causes it to strike and give one blow on the bell every hour.

The hammer itself is a permanent fixture and is set in the centre of its own arbor. The setting of the hammer spring is highly important. If it is set too stiffly, it can stop the clock when the lifting piece or the snail is about to rise.

Many 'one-at-the-hour' skeleton clocks have two pins on the minute wheel, causing the hammer to give a single blow for an hour and a single blow for the half hour. Others have four pins fitted, to make the clock strike a single blow at each quarter.

My firm belief is that all these clocks began life as 'one-at-the-hour' and clock repairers added the half and quarter hours to make them more animated. Confusion must certainly have reigned in some households with such frequent reminders of passing time!

Some thirty years later the 'one-at-the-hour' principle was again invoked, but this time the half hours were struck on an independent bell and the hours were struck on a gong.

All other striking mechanisms, whether hour or quarter, have no special features other than the usual trains found in any ordinary clock, except that they are visible in their frames.

Anchor, or recoil, and dead beat escapements predominated, while efforts at chronometer style, and detached escapements using helical and conical forms of balance springs, gave an added air of superiority to some clocks.

A number of movements employed duplex and gravity escapements – the latter appearing in three-, four-, and five-legged versions, not only competing with, but giving a splendour to the already growing line-up. Fig. 1-4 shows a gravity escapement clock and Fig. 2-18 is of a specimen with a grasshopper escapement.

Although the French used the pin-wheel escapement with enormous success in a great many of their clocks, skeleton and otherwise, this form did not find favour with English makers. Most English skeleton clocks with pin-wheel escapements were made in Birmingham, but the total number was very small.

Platform lever escapements, which were separately screwed to the frame, were common and employed either steel or solid brass balances. In many instances they were jewelled, as were the pallets (See Fig. 1-8).

Those incorporating the chronometer style of balance were compensated, and featured large rating nuts. This principle is shown in Fig. 1-9.

All skeleton clocks have ordinary pinion work to all trains. There are, however, a number of English and French skeleton clocks with helical gearing. One English maker concentrated on this type of gearing with some success, and is referred to later. One unidentified clock has lantern pinions.

Pendulums were invariably suspended by ribbon steel. The only silk thread or knife edge suspension I have seen came from an enthusiast and was never commercially exploited.

Clocks with music

It was only natural that in the skeleton clock formula, striking and chiming sequences could be shown at their very best. Cambridge and

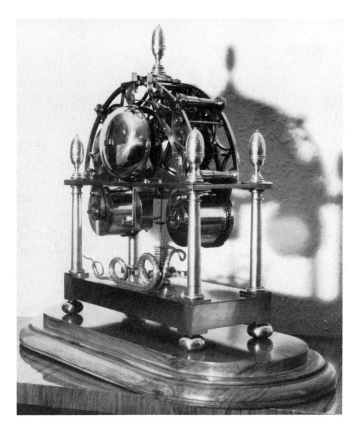

1-10 *Clock with balance and spring on the base*

Westminster chimes were outstanding favourites in the four-bell and later, four-gong array, with Whittington and St. Michaels being used for the eight-bell. Many clocks had combinations of both Westminster and Whittington, or any other eight-bell sequence. In this way, three or more changes could be made. This could be changed by hand on subsidiary dials to give the required selection.

As in conventional musical clocks, the tune could be selected by hand. In many cases, the musical selection had an automatic change which gave a different tune each day, bringing in a psalm or hymn for Sunday.

Although the sequences of chimes just described are the most common, many clocks had chimes peculiar to their area of origin. One such clock – in the Victoria Room at the Castle Museum, York, rings the Minster chimes on eight bells at each quarter.

The skeleton frame represents the West Front of York Minster, while a plaque on the marble base bears the following inscription:

'Presented by the Corporation of York for the best
Shorthorn Cow or Heifer exhibited at the Yorkshire
Fat Stock Show 1864, Won by John Radcliffe Stearsby,
York.'

The clock was presented to the York museum by Mr. J. R. Radcliffe – a relative of the original owner – in 1960.

Bells used in skeleton clocks more or less take the same hemispherical form and shape as those found in any ordinary English striking bracket or longcase clock. These are held with the customary one- or two-bell standards or brackets.

A rarity, sometimes encountered in cathedral skeleton clocks are true bells shaped like church bells. These can be one, two, or more, each silvered and each rings independently in the tower. This is achieved by connecting rods and linkages running up and carried to the required point in either the tower or the spire.

Bells were later superseded by steel wire gongs which were held by a massive gong standard. Heavy pieces of brass were used, on which were screwed equally heavy pieces of brass at the end of the gongs proper, in ones, twos, threes, fours, and even eights.

Even these brass blocks could not be left standardised and simple. They were fashioned into heart, shamrock, and *fleur-de-lis* designs. The Sarcelly Cross, shown in Fig. 3-40, was one design. The shapes reached farcical extremes when surmounted with spiral brass rods.

To prevent reverberation of the steel wire gong, and to give a non-metallic sound, leather was dovetailed into the face of the hammer head or, fitted into a round hole in the hammer face.

Extra decoration

The English skeleton clock gave manufacturers an unprecedented opportunity for indulging in decorations and embellishments to an almost unlimited extent.

Racks, rackhooks, lifting pieces, click springs, set-springs, and stop-work – all were carved, chased, engraved, scrolled, and flared into fantastic designs and shapes.

Not even the cocks, bridges, snails, and motion work escaped these embellishments. Hammer heads became battle axes, halberds, sword hilts, wheatsheafs, flowers, and human hands, while hammer arbors were turned to match the pillars which held the frames together.

The use of coiled and blued steel hammer springs in many cases gave a shimmering effect during the striking sequence.

Silent and strike mechanisms with pull repeat and numerous styles of subsidiary dials soon appeared, some minus their rings, which were

9

1-11 *Balance spring clock with columns, which were peculiar to Liverpool and Birmingham makers*

replaced by ribbon, scroll or tablet schemes. Platform rise and fall and set beat adjustments arrived in many combinations. All kinds of stop-work arrangements – including Geneva – were pressed into service for alarm systems. In fact, anything and everything that would enhance decoration and give a multiplicity of components was used. Pallets came in for the same treatment, some being jewelled. Other refinements were two, three, and four screws fastening escape and other wheels. See Fig. 3-19. Their collets on the arbors, together with six-spoked crossings to all wheels, gave them the appearance of a regulator clock.

For the going train, steel screwed endpieces of round and thistle design were nickel plated, their edges having a crimped pattern. Where platform escapements were used, these were, in some cases, beautifully jewelled, having large ruby pallet stones with equally large ruby impulse pins, all of which glistened with action.

Extra consideration was given to the balance spring, which was mainly flat or helical. One usually associates helical balance springs with chronometers only, but during the era of skeleton clock manufacture, much thought went into the train designs to incorporate escapements using helical balance-springs, as shown in Fig. 1-9.

The idea was extremely successful. The spring and its balance-wheel became the central focus of operation and it did away with the pendulum which made clocks sensitive to disturbance. The balance and spring were usually placed at the summit of the clock, or at its base.

The studs holding the balance-spring became exaggerated and ornate, many taking the shape of a long twisted serpent or lizard, the mouth being the portion to which the balance-spring was pinned. All were magnificently modelled in cast brass and gilt, the escapements being mounted vertically.

Early examples with a striking movement, an inverted lever escapement and a gilt serpent balance-spring stud holding the helical balance-spring, are shown in Figs. 1-10 and 1-11.

These have very long, separately cocked, balance staffs, approximately six inches long. Both top and bottom balance pivots are jewelled and have endstones, the pallets being of steel. The movement is entirely supported by four columns, the finials acting as screwheads to hold the baseplate. This form of column work is peculiar to Liverpool and Birmingham manufacturers.

As it grew in stature, the skeleton clock became more elaborate. Special refinements included maintaining power which was sometimes the eighteenth-century bolt and shutter system with segmented teeth. The fly or fan often was given three or four blades instead of the conventional two. Others were separately cocked, and had adjustable regulating vanes, not unlike a governor, to control the speed of striking. In the last phase, bevelled gearing was carried to the quarter and chiming trains. For further gimmickry, a fixed spirit level in a brass container became an extra accessory and was screwed in front on the base, with special large levelling slow motion brass thumb screws at each corner of the base to level the clock.

In the manufacture of some striking, large chiming, and musical skeleton clocks, it was often the practice to place an extra frame at the base. In most cases this was located in front and screwed to the main assembly. It was meant to depict the main porch or doorway and gave a three-dimensional appearance. Angled side frets or wings were used similarly when makers designed their frames, especially for striking mechanisms, the same frames were adaptable for both ordinary strike and chiming trains, as can be seen in Figs. 1-12 and 1-13.

1-13 *York Minster striking clock with flat side frets by J. Smith and Sons*

An example of a rosette collet can be seen in Fig. 2–15. All were blued, including the screws, to give an extra visual finish.

Even more decoration

The extravaganza was carried to further excess where the grand design ended in spires, turrets, pinnacles, minarets, pagodas, etc. Metal emblems were pinned at each point or placed into holes to carry flags, pennants, weather vanes, crosses, crescents, sailships, or dragons. These were but a few of the devices employed. They were fashioned in either brass or steel. The brass versions could be gilt or silvered, whilst the steel emblems were blued.

Many of these emblems had additional designs, while others were fretted out, the brass ones being engraved and carrying motifs. Positioned on spires or pinnacles they were very frail and could be caught easily after the glass shade was removed and when winding or dusting. Many an emblem must have been broken in this manner, leaving the stump in the frame. When emblems were not replaced, the broken parts were filed, ground, or polished flush with the tops of the holes, which were about half an inch deep.

If one looks at the clock in Fig. 1-14, it can be seen that the spires are separate castings, as distinct from the frame proper. They are supported by cross bars. Each spire carries a blued steel emblem just as it was sent out by the factory when it was made.

Fig. 1-15, however, shows an identical clock, but with three brass finials. These are a much later addition, the original emblems having been either discarded or lost.

A third identical clock shown in Fig. 1-16 has three brass balls at the summit of the spire. At first sight the spires of this clock appear shorter and thicker than might be expected. On removing one of the brass balls which had been screwed on, a hole was clearly exposed where once an emblem had been positioned. The owner has since had the emblems restored to their original condition.

The main structure of these three clocks is identical and indisputably they came from the same factory. Today they belong to the same owner. The trains are also identical, each wheel having six crossings or spokes, on both the going and striking trains. There is a slight variation in the design of the lifting pieces, snails, racks, and motion work, which illustrates the ways in which the basic design could be adapted. In Fig. 1-17, there are dragon emblems on the spires of an 1850 pagoda skeleton clock in the chinoise style by J. Smith of Clerkenwell, which belongs to Mr. J. W. Coe, of Horsham, Surrey.

Pivoted chain rollers of brass, to guide and take the strain of the fusee chains, were a further addition.

The majority of brass frames were polished and lacquered, and on fine quality movements they were frost gilt. The dozen or so chromium plated and oxidized skeleton clocks in existence are, of course, hybrids.

The frivolity continued when blue, green, or red coloured gut lines were employed, fusee chains were blued, and pinions undercut and given a mirror-like finish.

In their earliest form, the pillars were permanently seated and riveted into the back frame, which was standard practice. This was eventually superseded by all the pillars being screwed to both front and back frames, reverting to the French method. The screws had collets or washers, some of plain brass, some chamfered, some undercut, others domed. On later and finer quality movements steel collets were used, fashioned in star and rosette designs and, for further ornamentation, a smaller washer, similarly fashioned, was laid on top of each collet. A double washer resulted. Again this was an importation from the Continent.

1-15 *Lichfield clock with modified spire tops*

1-16 *Lichfield clock with modified spire tops*

1-14 *Lichfield Cathedral clock as made by J. Smith and Sons of Clerkenwell. No. 188 in their catalogue*

1-17 *Pagoda style clock by J. Smith and Sons with dragon emblems*

Not content with emblems to adorn the spires, some clockmakers slung finely meshed chainwork from pinnacle to pinnacle, and spire to spire, the ends culminating in metal tassels, similar to those worn on Victorian gentlemen's alberts or watchchains.

Original additions were cast figures dressed as courtiers, ladies, knights in armour, etc. These were set into niche-like parts of the frame, while reclining animals were placed at the base. The figures were positioned in both the front and rear frames, as can be seen in Fig. 3-40. All figures were gilt.

1-18 *Simple scroll frame 8-day clock*

1-19 *Clock going for a month, with a frame identical to 1-18*

at the top of the pendulum. The incorporation of rise and fall was a rare feature in skeleton work, but set beat adjustments became commonplace.

That the skeleton clock should strike an educational note is not altogether surprising when one considers its potentialities. The City of Liverpool Museum provides the following interesting information on a clock (Fig. 1-20) made by George Eccles of Liverpool in 1894, to the order of the Museums' committee, following a highly successful educational experiment in the 1880s. This entailed sending a clock movement round to various Liverpool schools to be assembled and set going in the classroom.

The committee, urged by the Rev. Henry H. Higgins, ordered a skeleton clock movement to be made to provide an educational display on the main museum staircase. The clock was destroyed by enemy action in 1941. The only picture of it in existence is that shown in Fig. 1-20.

A much more simple scroll frame is shown in Fig. 1-18. The clock is a fusee-wound timepiece that goes for eight days. Inscribed on the back frame is the name Barwise, London. In Fig. 1-19 is a timepiece driven by two fusees, which goes for a month. This clock bears the name John Pace. The frames of the two clocks are identical. Both clocks have their centre arbors planted at the apex of the front frame. The third and escape wheels in each case are held by a one-piece curved cock, the pallets being separately cocked.

The transformation from an eight-day timepiece to a one-month timepiece may be easily observed. The two barrels have been set at each side of the frames, at the lower scrolls, which show the ratchet and click set-up to their advantage. The two fusees are placed in the upper section. The additional wheel to make up the month sequence gears lies between the two fusees.

The adoption of different chapter rings and hands is a mere detail. Both clocks have solid cast brass bases and are dated *circa* 1840.

The pendulum

There was little, if any, variation in either the construction or design of the pendulum.

Lenticular (or lens) shape bobs were almost universally used. A few clocks had pewter and zinc cylindrical bobs which tended to look incongruous and clumsy when contrasted with the general structure (see Fig. 2-16). Mercurial pendulums were few and found only on high quality skeleton clocks. Flat brass or steel rods were the rule, although there was a small sprinkling of round wooden rods used mainly with cylindrical bobs.

Pendulums were suspended by ribbon steel and coarse time-keeping regulation was obtained from the rating nut below the pendulum bob. For finer adjustment, some clocks carried an additional thumb screw

Mr. Frederick Henry Eccles, son of George Eccles, provided these particulars:

Westminster chiming clock *circa* 1894 designed to illustrate various principles of clock work.

Going train: fitted with mainspring drive, fusee and chain, with maintaining power. Chronometer escapement beating seconds with compensation balance.

Striking train: weight driven, fitted with locking plate, and striking the hours on a large musical tube.

Quarter chiming train: weight driven, fitted with rack, and sounding quarter chimes on musical tubes.

Case: panelled mahogany with full-sized glazed door and glass side panels, allowing the mechanism to be easily seen.

Dial: engraved, silvered, 12-inch diameter.

Thus, by having mainspring drive, fusee and chain, countwheel for hour strike, rack for quarters, chronometer escapement with compensated balance, and weights, the clock almost completed the horological sequence. Small wonder that it was an educational success.

There are English skeleton clocks only a few inches high. These were the earliest made, and, with rosewood bases and carved feet, looked very elegant. The reverse might be said of those rising up to four feet and more.

Variations in dials

Dial work began in the orthodox manner with plain silvered engraved chapter rings. Eventually, the engraved dial was almost superseded by painted numerals. Some dials were painted in ordinary white with black figures, others were painted black to enable any coloured numeral required to be used, including gold and silver.

Next came the development of slightly decorated dials, the engraving being maintained and, in fact, being increased almost to the point of absurdity.

The dials finally became so exotically fretted, so over-engraved and embellished, that even from only a few feet away it was completely impossible to see the time. The seconds dial could hardly be seen in the maze, whilst the tin plate centre seconds hand could often only be distinguished from the ornate dial by being painted in colour, usually by its owner.

The dial was in most cases pinned to the front frame by three dial feet. These quite often were awkwardly planted in the most inaccessible places and near the vital part of the train or motion work.

The hands themselves were often cheap and shoddy in comparison with the rest of the fine workmanship. Many look incongruous, their tin plate appearance revealing that the nineteenth-century manufacturers did not emulate their forebears.

Was this epoch of clockmaking frivolous? Did it reach out of its depths? What functions did it perform and fulfil?

It certainly gave an impetus to the clock manufacturer and propagated trade and employment for some eighty years or more. It also left an indelible mark on its era. It gave the general public an appreciation of the clockmaker's art and attracted the individual who hitherto had not been caught by the 'horological bug'. The skeleton clock was, in addition, an excellent choice for presentations on special occasions.

One fact is known for certain – skeleton clocks never gained favour with ardent and serious antiquarian horologists, who were very adamant in their views. They have variously described it as 'trifling', 'monstrous', or 'hideous', and 'the creation of mad hatters'. Skeleton clocks were never regarded as objects of beauty. They were undoubtedly overshadowed by 'big names' of the past.

After the skeleton clock fashion began to die, one or two manufacturers tried to keep the flame alive. In one model, some attempt was made to give it a new look, as can be seen from the sketch from the 1910 illustrated catalogue of Smith & Son of St. John's Square, London, shown on the next page.

Deciding the origin

In determining the origin of English skeleton clocks, the best guide is the frame.

1-21 *Scroll frame clock labelled Monk of Bolton that may have been made by Edwards of Stourbridge*

1-22 *Back of clock shown above*

The pattern, design, and overall style and shape are the points which may reveal its source. It is not unusual to find many examples of skeleton clocks bearing names other than makers. Certain styles were not just peculiar to an area alone, but to a particular manufacturer.

In assessing the importance of a skeleton clock, one must have, and use, good judgement and take into account all the salient features before arriving at a final decision, just as an art expert does in relation to an unsigned painting.

It has been argued that identification by a pattern or design credited to a specific maker might not always be infallible, since one maker could have copied from another. This only happened in rare instances since manufacturers jealously guarded their patterns and designs which, after all, were the hallmark of their success.

Dials and chapter rings are no criterion to judge by. The plain engraved chapter rings are deemed to be the earliest in skeleton clocks, but all makers, in fact, used them. Similarly, the same manufacturers who produced plain rings later turned out the over-fretted dials.

There are few characteristics to look for in clock trains. All makers tended to employ five or six crossings or spokes to the wheels, as they did to some of the fusee great wheels in higher quality clocks. These refinements were not the prerogative of one manufacturer or another. Trains of gears are therefore not a reliable guide.

Striking mechanisms are not satisfactory as a guide either. Embellishment to the racks, lifting pieces, etc., was equally rife in the north of England, the Midlands, and in London. Except in one or two special instances, one cannot identify any specific maker through the escapement either. It is known, however, that some makers – mainly from Liverpool – concentrated on a form of chronometer escapement for skeleton clocks. Others used the pin-wheel escapement, which stemmed from Birmingham.

Numbers of both these types were infinitesimal compared with the anchor (recoil) escapement which predominated and was used by every maker, important and otherwise. Some dead beat escapements were employed in better quality skeleton clocks but these were few in number.

The platform escapement, although not so common, was used by all

sections of the clockmaking community and again, was not confined to any individual maker.

One slight consolation remains to the investigator – that the majority of skeleton movements supported by columns or pillars, usually standing upon large plinths, are the products of the Midlands and Lancashire.

Having dealt with the probable points of recognition, let us examine a clock of which the maker may be identified beyond doubt.

Fig. 3-29 shows an example of a 'one-at-the-hour' skeleton clock as described in the 1865 catalogue of J. Smith & Sons, of Clerkenwell – a firm which became one of the largest producers of skeleton clocks.

Figs. 3-38 and 3-39 show a clock purporting to be the work of G. A. Biddell. It can be readily seen that this clock is similar in every detail to that shown in the Smiths' catalogue. The Biddell clock is also a 'one-at-the-hour' strike, and has an identical frame design, dial, and halberd hammer head.

A final interesting fact is that the escutcheon plate with the name 'G. A. Biddell, maker, London' has been placed over the frame decoration. A maker normally incorporates the nameplate into his design or, in the majority of cases, places it on the base.

The examination of the frame should be the deciding factor when making an identification. To illustrate this point, turn to Figs. 3-11 and 3-12, which show a scroll frame design skeleton clock made by a recorded maker, James Edwards of Stourbridge, Worcs.

Discounting the flint glass centres and treating this clock as having ordinary train, it can be seen that, apart from the scroll pattern, the frame has a slender waist and rises and ends at the top in a triangular formation with curved terminals, coupled with finely turned robust pillar work.

Compare this work with the slightly smaller clock, also a timepiece, shown in Figs. 1-21 and 1-22. There is a great similarity. The chapter ring of the second clock bears the name John Monk, Bolton, Lancashire. Observe the frames carefully and compare them.

The well-designed scrolled frames are identical and end in a triangular form. They have the same generously turned pillars, the same slender waists and styles of cup upon which the movement rests. These are the facts upon which to base a judgement.

There are no records in any reference works of a John Monk of Bolton as a clockmaker. The possibility that this clock was the product of James Edwards cannot be ruled out. He was a maker in a considerable way, and it is likely that this particular pattern of frame was exclusive to him, as was the Scott Memorial clock to Evans of Handsworth.

Who were the makers?

A problem arises when trying to separate the work of two reputable clock establishments, for example, Dwherrihouse, Ogston & Bell, and

1-24 *Dial details of the clock in 1-23*

1-25 *Pin-wheel escapement of the clock in 1-24. The coup-perdu pallet is on the curved arm*

Viner & Co., both of London. Both makers produced a skeleton clock incorporating a pin-wheel escapement, as shown in Figs. 1-23 and 1-26. Each frame is of rafter construction and, except for a slight deviation in the cross members, the clocks are identical, as are the plinths upon which the movements rest.

It is probably not mere coincidence that both have the same one-piece hour and seconds ring, again only with a slight deviation. It is shown well in Fig. 1-24.

As far as escapement arrangements are concerned, the clock by Viner & Co. has orthodox fixed pallets (Fig. 1-27) to its pin-wheel whilst the Dwherrihouse, Ogston & Bell pin-wheel escapement embraces a 'coup perdu', which enables the seconds hand to miss a beat and jump

every second although the pendulum beats half seconds. Fig. 1-25 shows the pivoted pallet with its counterpoise, which causes the missed beat.

One significant feature that these two clocks have in common is that the ratchet set up has an 'extra' in that it employs a cock. This is a little unusual for English clocks since this section is normally pinned.

Fig. 1-28 shows a third clock, which has an identical frame to that of the Viner clock, and base plinths identical with those of both clocks just considered. A simple but pleasing scalloped edge dial enhances the frame. The clock has a half dead beat escapement with maintaining power. It is unsigned.

All three clocks are timepieces, go for eight days, and are *circa* 1845.

These frame patterns were a product of Birmingham and obviously

1-28 *Another clock with anchor escapement, but a frame similar to 1-23 and 1-26*

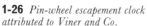

1-26 *Pin-wheel escapement clock attributed to Viner and Co.*

acceptable to all makers. Only one manufacturer has been traced who specialised in the making and incorporation of the pin-wheel escapement into English clocks. This was the firm of Wray & Son, also of Birmingham, which flourished from 1840 to 1886.

In general heavily fretted skeleton frames were peculiar to London manufacturers. The column-support incorporating the escapement with a balance and hairspring within the train, were peculiar to Liverpool (See Fig. 1-10). Platform escapements are not included in this category.

The remaining half-dozen locations north of the Midlands restricted themselves to producing timepieces only and, in consequence, the variety of patterns was limited, the frames being of rafter design. Not only did makers produce their own individual patterns and schemes, but more often than not, copied other makers' efforts, often with slight modification.

Of the countless thousands of skeleton clocks that were produced in this country and flooded the markets, more than half were manufactured in the Clerkenwell area of London. Of the remainder, the greater portion was made by Birmingham manufacturers, and the lesser by other makers spread over the rest of the country.

400-*day clocks*

Year skeleton clocks (or those of even longer duration) that were manufactured in England are a source of mystery. Records show that the undermentioned have year clocks against their names:

R. D. Feltham of Jersey.	(Silversmith.)
James Lamb of Bicester.	(General stores, clocks, glass, china, earthenware, etc.)
John Pace of Bury St. Edmunds.	(Silversmith, dealer in clocks, watches, etc.)
H. Pike of London.	(Clockmaker.)
J. L. W. Smith & Sons.	(Clock manufacturers.)
Benjamin Parker of Bury St. Edmunds.	(His name cannot be traced in any watch or clock reference works, for the simple reason that he was a gunsmith.)

The first five in the list exhibited 400-day skeleton clocks at the Great Exhibition of 1851 in London. Two such 400-day clocks are shown in Chapter 7 dealing with year clocks. Figs. 7-4 and 7-6 have engraved upon their brass bases the name of B. Parker, Bury St. Edmunds.

Mr. Adrian Allen, Assistant Archivist to the Bury St. Edmunds and West Suffolk Records Office, provided the following information regarding B. Parker.

Benjamin Parker, a gunsmith by profession, was one of the Baptist Trustees named in a conveyance of the land upon which the Baptists Chapel stands, 1834.

1839 Pigot's Directory. Benjamin Parker, gun maker, 30 Churchgate Street.

1844 White's Directory. Benjamin Parker, gun maker, Chalk Lane.

1855 White's Directory. Benjamin Parker, gun maker, 9, Chalk Lane.

He appears to have been the son of Benjamin Parker, a gunsmith of Bury St. Edmunds, who died well-off in 1826, and who lived in Churchgate Street. The second Parker bequeathed his house, other property, his stock in trade and implements to his son Benjamin. Incidentally, the Curator of the Clock Museum at Bury St. Edmunds has no knowledge of a B. Parker.

There is a third 400-day skeleton clock in Ohio, in America, which is identical to the B. Parker clock in Fig. 7-6. Each carries two subsidiary dials (1 to 52 for the weeks, and 1 to 30 for the date calendar). Engraved on the Ohio clock in a similar manner, however, is the name John Pace, Bury St. Edmunds.

1-29 *English scroll clock with French style going barrel and great wheel*

The clock has been verified and seen by two well-known American collectors of clocks, but regrettably, I was unable to obtain any photographs.

A fourth 400-day clock owned by J. L. W. Smith & Sons, of Clerkenwell, was destroyed in the London blitz.

After four years of intensive search these were the only 400-day clocks that came to light.

What have these 400-day skeleton clocks in common?

All have identical frames of scroll design, all are timepieces, and have similar trains and carry the large thirty-two-leaved pinion that meshes with the two fusees. They have four barrels, curved cocks, etc., and all are wound from the rear. They have fretted Arabic dials (note the fancy decoration). There are however small differences in the layout and arrangement of calendar mechanisms – a mere detail to any large manufacturer who was geared up for this versatility – and in the brass bases.

The escapements were anchor (or recoil).

Who were the creators of these 400-day skeleton clocks? Scanning once more through the list of six names, by far the strongest candidate is J. L. W. Smith & Sons (John, Lancelot, William), of St. Johns Square, Clerkenwell. They were already a great force in the clock industry and were responsible for both the designing and for the manufacturing of long duration clocks. Their big resources made them a self-contained unit, manufacturing everything on the premises.

The story of their superiority is told by an observer of the *Illustrated London News* in Chapter 3.

Continental influence

The Continent had some influence on English design. The scroll clock in Fig. 1-29 has a going barrel instead of a fusee and the French system of a large toothed wheel to obtain long duration. Although it bears the famous names of Mudge and Dutton, London, it is doubtful whether they made it. The clock is owned by Mr. R. M. Burton of Whitwell on the Hill, York.

Fig. 1-30 shows a month pendulum clock in the collection of Dr. S. P. Lehv of New York. The Y-frame is French in style, but the movement has an English fusee drive and the train wheels are orthodox.

The reign of the English skeleton clock practically ended towards the close of the nineteenth century. None were made for commercial purposes after 1913-14. There are, however, isolated exceptions of individual production, some clocks still being devised by individual clockmakers and private persons up to the present day.

Electrical drive

Even electric skeleton clocks were made towards the end of the century, and its makers tried to turn it into a commercial proposition.

The decline of the mechanically-wound skeleton clock must have given the Shepherds Patent Electric skeleton clock from Leadenhall Street, London, a fillip. The clock, shown in Figs. 1-31 and 1-32, is a seconds impulse slave clock. In place of the usual brass cups or feet, which support the frame, are four red velvet-covered electro-magnets. Each pair of magnets is energised every second to attract the ends of a steel beam, pivoted in the centre. The motion is transmitted to an anchor escapement which drives a thirty-toothed escape-wheel. According to its owner, Mr. George Duncan of Norwich, the clock is extremely noisy.

Time-signal clocks

Time signals from the Royal Greenwich Observatory were distributed to London and other parts of the country on an increasing scale from 1853. Their records show that by 1865 signals were sent every hour to

1-31　　　　　　　　　　　　　**1-32**

1-33

1-34

the office of the London District Telegraph Co. and made available to chronometer makers.

This caused a number of clock manufacturers to design electric clocks which could accept this signal, one of these being The British Telegraph and Manufacturing Co. Ltd. Some of their clocks on the Wheatstone principle (the two earliest forms of electric clock were the Bain principle and the Wheatstone principle) had already been on trial at the G.P.O.

Of great significance is a letter from the Office of Works, to the then Astronomer Royal, G. B. Airy, dated December 1, 1875, containing a request for his opinion on the British Telegraph Company's claim that their clocks would be most suitable for use in the Central Telegraph Office. Airy went as far as to say 'that under the circumstances, I prefer Cooke's for the Post Office'.

The clock shown in Figs. 1-33 and 1-34 gives some idea of the type of clock utilised for this purpose by the British Telegraph Co.

The original electrical controls have been replaced by a going barrel and lever escapement. However the main structure is original. The dial with its skeleton form of motion work and finely-cut wheels is supported by gilt columns. The base is magnificently engraved and, in the centre amongst the wealth of pattern can be seen the words 'The British Telegraph Manufacturing Co. Ltd.'. The clock is from the collection of Mr. Norman Langmaid, Washington, U.S.A., and he and Mr. Gerry Planus, of London, provided the picture.

Today skeleton clocks have regained some of their popularity. The antique boutiques, together with the antique markets, are placing more worthy prices on their heads. The salerooms, following suit, must now give encouragement to the many owners by making them aware that their clocks are again becoming a status symbol. Glass shades are to be had, although at a premium, and the back room boys are trekking to the four points of the compass to unearth forgotten treasures.

1-31 *and* **1-32** *Electric skeleton clock*

1-33 *and* **1-34** *Electric skeleton clock for receiving time signals, now converted to spring drive*

CHAPTER 2

SOME ENGLISH SKELETON CLOCKS

One-at-the-hour clocks

Second only to the ordinary skeleton timepiece in popularity was undoubtedly the one-at-the-hour strike skeleton clock, thousands of which still exist. The output of this type of clock was considerable because of its simple construction. It was the poor man's striking clock – therefore the commonest – without any complicated mechanism that could go wrong. In spite of its single blow, it gave at least some warning of the hour. Every maker, large and small, produced this kind of clock, which could be bought for as little as three pounds.

The clocks appeared in many designs and sizes, and usually incorporated an anchor escapement. In the slightly better qualities dead beat escapements were employed, and some even had the distinction of possessing chronometer escapements.

The most popular, and most easily recognised, one-at-the-hour skeleton clock took the form shown in Figs. 3-38 and 3-39. This is the heart-shaped scroll design frame at its simplest, although, in contrast, it has an exotically fretted dial, together with a halberd hammer head. The movement rests on a plain white marble oval base.

This particular example was the product of J. Smith & Sons of St. John's Square, Clerkenwell, and was shown in their 1865 catalogue.

What can best be described as the arabesque design is used in the one-at-the-hour fusee wound timepiece, bearing the name E. W. Chinn, seen in Fig. 2-1. This type of scroll design suggests a delicacy of pattern which is rarely present in normal skeleton work.

From the front it appears that the ratchet set-up and click are between the frames. The front is actually a shortened skeletonised dial frame matching in every detail the main frames behind it, to which the pierced dial is screwed. The side view in Fig. 2-2, clearly shows this assembly, together with the dial feet entering the front frame.

The train is planted in a vertical row, all its wheels, including the

2-2 *The separate dial frame of the clock in 2-1 can be seen at the bottom*

motion work, having six crossings or spokes. A recoil escapement is employed and a steel fusee cap is screwed to the fusee cone. The cylindrical pendulum bob is of pewter, the wooden rod being made of oak. The striking hammer is formed like a halberd, the bell standard being screwed into the top pillar. A normal bell is used. The main frames are screwed and colleted to the pillars, both front and rear. The Roman numerals, set on shields to the pierced dial, give a pleasing contrast to the tracery behind. The steel hands have the same formation as the Sarcelly Cross. This clock goes for eight days without winding and it is dated *circa* 1850. It is the property of Dr. Jo E. Anderson of 126 So. Fourth Street, Le Suer, Minnesota, U.S.A.

Dr. Anderson says: 'E. W. Chinn in old (Huddersfield) Directories made his appearance in 1853 under the description of "watch and clock-maker at 11 Market Walk". Ten years later he moved to 9 John William Street and was still listed as being there in 1873–1876, but there is no listing for 1879. The Directories after 1845 did not distinguish between clock and watchmakers and tradesmen.

'A knowledgeable jeweller in Huddersfield (now retired) told my informant that he recalls his father mentioning the name and that Chinn was a merchant who put his name on the goods he sold. He definitely was *not* a clockmaker.'

The one-at-the-hour skeleton clock shown in Fig. 2-3 is in complete contrast to that just described. The design, being in simple but sober proportions, leaves the dial in clear relief against the thirteenth century style scrollwork on the frames. The frames themselves are screwed and colleted to the pillars front and rear, the brass collets being undercut. All the wheels in the train, including the motion work, have six crossings or spokes. The clock employs a dead beat escapement and goes for eight days. The fine narrow chapter ring is in the traditional early English style.

The dial is silvered and engraved with Roman numerals, a pair of fine steel *fleur-de-lis* hands adding to its elegance. An acorn finial holds the bell in place and the hammer head is of tulip design. The clock, which stands on a brass base and has brass bun feet was made around 1835.

A brass plaque bearing the name Bunyan & Gardner, Market Place, Manchester, is screwed to the edge of the base. The clock is from the collection of Major Anthony Heathcote, of Cheyne Walk, London.

It is generally assumed that one-at-the-hour skeleton clocks were of eight-day duration, but Fig. 2-4 shows an excellent example of a one-at-the-hour skeleton timepiece, which goes for a month at each winding. The first point to note is the well-proportioned scrolled frame. The movement is robust, the frames being a quarter of an inch thick and showing to great advantage the finely turned pillars screwed to the frames front and rear (seen in Fig. 2-5) and resting on cupped feet. Incidentally the brass frames have been silvered at a later date. The fine

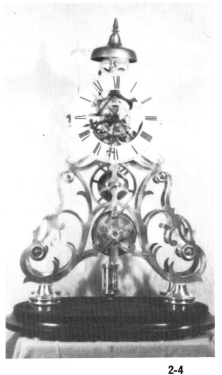

2-4 *and* 2-5 *'One-at-the-hour' clock that runs for a month*

2-6 *and* 2-7 *'One-at-the-hour' with chronometer escapement*

caliper steel pallets denote that the clock has a dead beat escapement. There is an excellent but plain silvered engraved chapter ring with Roman numerals. A halberd-styled hammer strikes the one blow on a bell at each hour. The movement is some 20 inches high, 13 inches wide, and 4 inches deep.

This month clock has a centre seconds hand and is of exceptionally high quality. It is unsigned, but London made, and is *circa* 1840. It is from the collection of Mr. Norman Langmaid of Washington D.C., U.S.A.

Chronometer escapement

At first glance the one-at-the-hour skeleton clock shown in Fig. 2-6 appears to be of unusual elevation. This effect is achieved by its tall, slender proportions and the fact that its height is approximately four times its width.

Three unique features may be found in it. Firstly it incorporates a form of chronometer escapement (shown in Fig. 2-7) complete with compensated balance and helical balance-spring. Secondly, it has an elaborate, yet crude, striking hammer arrangement, rods and linkages, to motivate the single blow at the hour and, lastly, the mainspring barrel is planted independently from the main train and is suspended by two inverted brass plates which are screwed from under the brass platform upon which the movement rests.

The frame is of simple design, the movement being supported by four fluted columns. The one piece silvered dial showing the hours and seconds is signed Andrew Black, Alloa. On the inner rim of the hour chapter ring, stretching from the numerals eight to four, appears the word 'chronometer'.

The clock goes for eight days and has maintaining power. It stands $11\frac{1}{2}$ inches high, 4 inches wide, 3 inches deep and is dated *circa* 1840. It is also from the Norman Langmaid collection.

Of similar proportions to the clock shown in Fig. 2-6 is that in Fig. 2-8. It is yet another version of the one-at-the-hour strike. The movement is supported by columns or pillars, the bases of which rest on plinths. The elongated style of this clock is characteristic of north of England work.

On the movement there is very little to say, other than that it has a 60 tooth escape wheel – the pallets embracing a span of 20 teeth and the

2-9 *and* **2-10** *Typical English 8-day, 3-train, scroll clock made in Clerkenwell but since modified*

2-9

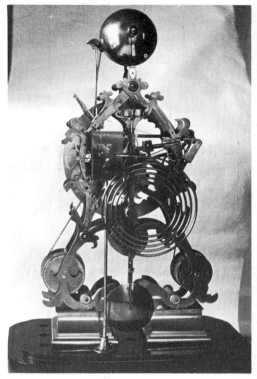

2-10

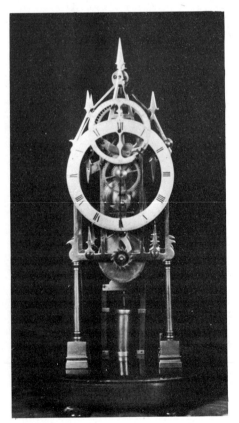

2-8 *Characteristic north of England 'one-at-the-hour'*

escapement is dead beat with a mercurial pendulum. The movement alone stands 13 inches high, is 5½ inches wide, and 3¾ inches in depth.

The established form of frame – usually the brass – has been silvered, and the one-piece double dial, showing the hours and seconds, is gilt. The bell has been removed for photography. The clock is unsigned, goes for eight days and is dated *circa* 1840. The clock is another of Mr. Langmaid's collection.

Typical English design

Fig. 2-9 shows an excellent example of an English three train eight-day skeleton clock in a simple scroll design. It is from the collection of Mr. Charles Allix of Bradbourne Farm, Sevenoaks, Kent, and can best be described in his own words:

'This clock could have been made at any time between about 1840 to perhaps 1860. It is highly characteristic of good English skeleton work of the period. Typical features are the ebonised wood base, the cast brass moulded and made-up plinths, upon which rest the movement, the style and shape of the frames, the *fleur-de-lis* finials, the generally florid excrescences and the skeletonised silvered chapter ring, with Roman numerals and scroll pattern on the inside edges. It is not particularly easy to see the time!

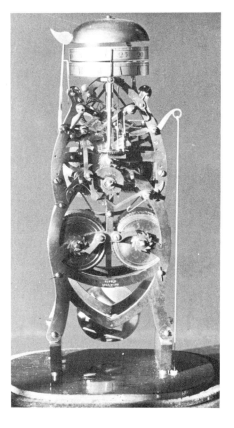

2-11 *Egg-shaped, but English, with French method of showing time*

'The clock, complete with its base and with a very fine glass shade, stands approximately 27 inches high. The wood base is pierced with nine holes to let out the sound of the quarter chimes which are struck on eight bells. The holes are backed with red silk to prevent dust, etc., from seeping in. The hours are struck very slowly and sonorously on a gong carried by a standard behind the pendulum.

'Engraved on the bell standard is a note that the clock was converted by "Norris", of "Notting Hill, London". To what does this refer? I think to a conversion from bell to striking on a gong, in which case the clock may be earlier than at first appears. Such a conversion is quite a "job", and almost invariably involves train alterations to prolong the intervals between the blows of the hammer.

'In this clock the comparatively heavy pendulum beats half seconds. The escapement is the half-dead beat type often used in late English spring driven wall clocks with short pendulums, and also noticeably a favourite escapement for skeleton clocks. The three trains have "reversed" fusees, and their long runs of chains look rather dangerous.

'The trains in count are evidently those of the English wall bracket clock of the period, the fusees having sixteen turns and the pinions of eight being employed. All wheels including those of the motion work have five or six crossings.

'The clock is far more compact than most English three train skeleton clocks, which are apt to sprawl and to emulate Victorian Gothic-revival architecture. Most of the steel work in this clock is finished white; but some is blued, such as the ornamental collars behind the pillar screws and the collars of the ratchet set-ups.

'The chain of the hour striking train runs over a roller on a frame pillar. It seems that the maker must have either preferred this arrangement to taking the chain from the other side of the barrel, or else have found too late that the pillar got in the way. In spite of the roller a very weak mainspring suffices. The fine appearance of this clock is completed by its crest of bells, each flanked by a long hammer.'

In fact, this is a London-made clock which was produced by J. Smith & Sons of St. John's Square, Clerkenwell. In Fig. 2-10 it can be seen that the wire steel gong has been introduced at a later date. Note the cumbersome hammer cock, and the differently shaped hour hammer head, not to speak of the crudely made-up gong standard which the manufacturers would certainly not have allowed to pass unchecked. The clock was made between 1830 and 1840.

The clock shown in Fig. 2-11 has been described as having an egg-shaped frame. It displays an unusual trend in English skeleton clock design. There is a possibility that its creator was influenced by the

2-14 *Compensated pendulum of 2-13*

Peering through the top of the movement, in Fig. 2-12 one can see the bevel gear drive. There are caliper pallets and escape-wheel, indicating that the clock has a dead beat escapement, beating half seconds. Maintaining power has also been installed. The name Rippin, Spalding, is stamped at the base of the frame.

The clock goes for eight days and is dated *circa* 1840. It is from the collection of Mr. R. Mc.V. Weston of Reigate, Surrey.

Detent escapements

Three excellent examples of the detached detent escapement skeleton clock, each different in its own sphere, are briefly described in this section. In the clock shown in Fig. 2-13, the frame is of a delicate scroll pattern and gives an entirely new interpretation of the English regulator dial, with its three distinct hour, minute, and seconds rings. The hours are denoted in tablet form, the minute ring might be described as 'lacey', and the seconds ring is plain and conventional.

Fig. 2-14 gives a rear view of this clock, showing the compensated

Louis XVI period when the time was often shown on French clocks by rotating circles or rings upon which the hours, minutes, and seconds were engraved or painted.

In this instance only hour and minute rings, which are silvered, have been included. A clear view is provided of the going and striking trains, and of the bevelled drive from the cannon pinion leading up to the minute wheel.

A humorous but original touch has been introduced by the maker. The silent and strike lever, top left of the picture, has been fashioned in the form of a leg, complete with boot, and another lever is made in the shape of a monster. The clock strikes only the hours.

2-15

2-16

2-17 Detent escapement clock which chimes on eight bells

cylindrical pendulum, the inverted train, and the crossed-out fusee great wheel. It is from the collection of Dr. S. P. Lehv of New York.

In Fig. 2-15, we return to the orthodox fretted scroll frame, again of delicate proportions. This specimen gives a better idea of the escapement lay-out and employs the same type of cylindrical pendulum as the previous clock, as shown in Fig. 2-16. The clock is from the collection of Dr. MacRae, London.

A rare feature of the detent escapement skeleton clock shown in Fig. 2-17 is its three-train quarter chime, striking the quarters on eight bells and the hours on a gong. As with the other two detent clocks, the

2-18 *Rare skeleton with grasshopper escapement*

2-19

2-20

2-19 *Scroll clock with chronometer escapement with crown wheel (shown in 2-20)*

going train is inverted. The scroll frame has been especially constructed to accommodate the strike and quarter striking barrels, independently from their trains proper, thus somewhat accentuating the enormous length of chain reaching from the barrel to the fusee. A cylindrical pendulum is used. The movement stands 21 inches high, 13 inches wide, and is 5 inches in depth. There are blue steel rosette washers on the three ratchet set-ups.

A plate bears the name of C. C. Lowe, Manchester, and the clock is again from Mr. Langmaid's collection.

In this trio of clocks with detached detent escapements, whilst the pendulum registers a beat of half seconds, it records the full seconds upon the seconds dial. The three clocks have maintaining power and were made in London around 1850–60.

A rare specimen of the skeleton clock, of exceptional quality and embracing a grasshopper escapement, is shown in Fig. 2-18. This form of escapement, although thought to be the invention of John Harrison was introduced earlier by his brother, James Harrison, who incorporated the principle in one or more longcase clocks. The escapement in this particular clock is based on the method of John Harrison.

The independent chapter rings for the hours, minutes, and seconds, add dignity to a clock whose proportions, the manner in which it is set upon its four columns and its mercurial pendulum, make it a fine specimen. The clock has maintaining power, which can be seen through the spoked-out fusee great wheel. It goes for eight days, is signed Walsh of Reading, and is *circa* 1850. It is from the collection of the Franklin Institute, Philadelphia, U.S.A.

The skeleton clock with detent escapement on Fig. 2-19 showing the escape-wheel cut in the manner of a verge crown wheel once more emphasises the advantage to horological enthusiasts of the visible approach. The clock of eight-day duration has a fine scrolled designed frame, and is finely gilt, the escapement follows the layout developed by Thomas Earnshaw for marine chronometers. The impulse is in a notch in a steel roller and the discharge pallet is let into the collet of the steel balance-wheel. (See Fig. 2-20.)

The balance-wheel is in brass with steel timing screws. There are no compensating timing refinements as found on a marine chronometer. Fig. 2-20 clearly shows the helical hair-spring. The clock goes for eight days, has maintaining power, and stands only $8\frac{1}{2}$ inches high. The dial is silvered, the steel hands having a *fleur-de-lis* pattern, the movement carries the name Wm. Thomson, Dalkeith, and is *circa* 1850. The clock is from the collection of Mr. J. W. Coe, Walton-on-Thames, Surrey.

A skeleton regulator clock is shown in Fig. 2-21. It is of high quality. The rear view in Fig. 2-22 clearly shows the independent suspension for the pendulum away from the clock mechanism, which is based on a beam

2-21

2-22

2-23

2-24 *Lyre design*

2-25 *York Minster influence*

2-24

2-25

supported by two brass pillars. The side view in Fig. 2-23 shows the extent of the pallets, the strong suspension, and beat adjustment. The fusee great wheels are spoked out, and maintaining power is provided.

The clock features the normal layout for a regulator dial. It can also be seen that the movement is of rafter construction with slight frets, the whole assembly resting on eight brass matching cups. It goes for eight days, is unsigned, London-made, and *circa* 1850. It is from the Hawkins collection, Canterbury.

More designs

Fig. 2-24 shows a fine quality lyre-design fusee skeleton timepiece with three straight bars fashioned as lyre strings. The clock has an anchor escapement and goes for eight days. The frame is of sturdy proportions, the pillars are of robust formation, and the neat silvered chapter ring gives a clear reading. The clock is only 8 inches high, the movement itself being only 5/16 inches. The whole assembly, with its brass baseplate, rests on a fine oval rosewood base, on the front of which is brass inlay work with a rose motif.

The clock, which is signed Simmons & Co., Quadrant, Regent Street, and is dated *circa* 1825–30, is from the collection of Mr. Albert Odmark of Seattle, U.S.A.

Fig. 2-25 shows an hour striking skeleton clock depicting York Minster. This has additional frames which are attached to the main front frame, and accommodate the dial. A further frame portrays the porch, the whole giving a three-dimensional effect. The rear view in Fig. 2-26 shows the cocked variable fly, or fan, and steel wire gong, with its hatchet shaped hammer. The clock was made by J. Smith & Sons of St. John's Square, Clerkenwell, is *circa* 1850, and goes for eight days. It is from the collection of Major Anthony Heathcote, of London.

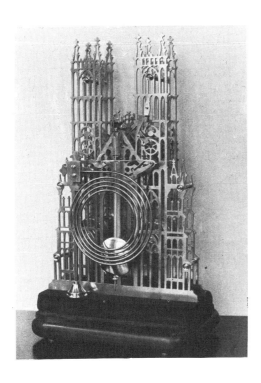

2-26 *Back of the clock in 2-25*

2-27 *Ivy-leaf design*

The timepiece shown in Fig. 2-27 has an anchor escapement with an ivy leaf pattern which is repeated in the frame. It will be observed that the plain chapter ring is already being phased out, and supplanted by an early form of skeleton dial. This transition took place between the 1830s and 1850s.

The eight-day movement rests on a rectangular mahogany base, the design of the mother of pearl inlay matches the frame design. The clock is *circa* 1830 and is from the collection of Mr. E. Hitchcock of Canterbury.

Fig. 2-28 shows a fourteen-day striking fusee skeleton clock made by J. Wallis of Tabernacle Walk, Finsbury Square, with a rafter frame. An unusual feature is that the four terminals in the frame casting have been used as feet to support the main assembly. Unique also are the spoked out fusee ratchet and great wheels. An anchor escapement is employed and a

2-29 *Rafter construction with dead-beat escapement*

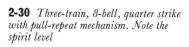

2-30 *Three-train, 8-bell, quarter strike with pull-repeat mechanism. Note the spirit level*

2-31 *The balance-wheel is at the top, with serpent-shaped balance-spring stud*

slight brass inlay can be seen on the wooden base. The clock goes for eight days and was made in 1830. It is from the collection of Mr. C. H. Rycroft of Halifax.

The striking skeleton clock made by John Blaylock of Carlisle, shown in Fig. 2-29 emphasises with great simplicity the rafter construction method. Except for the fretting of the hour snail, the clock is devoid of any frills or embellishments but at the same time the whole mechanism can be seen in great detail. The clock uses a dead beat escapement and the pallets span the top frame pillar, the escape-wheel lying directly underneath. It has maintaining power and goes for eight days. It incorporates a spirit level and is *circa* 1830.

John Blaylock, of Carlisle, is shown in Baillie's reference book, *Watchmakers and Clockmakers of the World*, as working in the early nineteenth century. The clock is from the collection of Mr. C. B. Reeve of Hastings.

Fig. 2-30 shows an important and very fine quality three-train, eight-bell quarter chiming clock, the hours being struck on a steel wire gong. The frame, which is of scroll design, gives an unhindered view of the whole mechanism. The movement stands on plinths. The clock has a dead beat escapement and pull repeat, and incorporates a spirit level. It has a very clear silvered chapter ring with Roman numerals. The clock is signed Roskell, Liverpool – the name of a famous family of clock and watchmakers in that town. It is dated *circa* 1840 and is from the collection of Mr. James McGarva of Chester.

Fig. 2-31 shows a movement supported on four pillars. The feature of the clock is the large solid steel balance wheel with three rating nuts and its helical hair-spring. The hair-spring stud is fashioned in the shape of a serpent and is fixed to a form of potence seen projecting from the backplate.

2-32 *Typical London clock*

2-34 *Congreve rolling-ball clock*

The clock has a lever escapement and a unique feature is a shaped piece projecting from the end of the potence which passes through an aperture of a one-piece steel pallet to prevent the escapement from overbanking.

The clock goes for eight days and has maintaining power. It is probably Liverpool made. It is unsigned but was made about 1840 and is in the collection of Major Anthony Heathcote, London.

The glass shade does not impair the beauty of the working mechanism, but if well selected adds to the clock's appearance as shown in Figs. 2-32 and 2-33.

Fig. 2-32 is an ordinary London-made fusee timepiece with scrolled design and fretted dial, *circa* 1860. The clock in Fig. 2-33 is a one-at-the-hour strike, a product of the Midlands. The original hammer spring has been replaced by a very ordinary spiral spring, and, unusual for English skeleton clocks, there is a French type of chapter ring complete with bezel. The clock is dated about 1850.

Both pictures are reproduced by courtesy of the Henry Ford Museum, Dearborn, Michigan, U.S.A.

The final picture in this chapter, Fig. 2-34, shows a Congreve rolling ball clock, which could be regarded as a form of skeleton clock. Numerous copies of Congreve's original clock of 1808 have been made both commercially and by enthusiastic amateurs. The time-keeping device is a ball bearing that runs in a zig-zag track which is tilted each time the ball arrives at the end. This particular clock is also in the Henry Ford Museum, Dearborn, Michigan, U.S.A.

CHAPTER 3

ENGLISH SKELETON CLOCK MANUFACTURERS

Evans of Birmingham

A brief history of some manufacturers and their individual styles and designs may provide the reader with a guide to recognising unnamed clocks.

One maker with a prolific output was William Frederick Evans, of the Soho Factory, Handsworth, Birmingham, the designer of the now famous Scott Memorial skeleton clock. He was also responsible for the very large number of skeleton clocks one sees with a detached detent escapement. Under his aegis, the factory became one of the largest clock establishments in the United Kingdom.

Were it not for an unusual romance, the skeleton clock designed like Scott's Memorial in Edinburgh, which was shown at the Great Exhibition of 1851, might never have come into being.

In 1805, the famous firm of Boulton & Watt founded their business having especial connections with the Royal Mint. The engineering departments grew so rapidly that they decided to give up the manufacture of clocks, which hitherto had been an important branch of their work. When they took this step, one of their clock employees was John Houghton (see Fig. 3-1). He was a man of much perseverance and ability and, realising that here was an opening with a great potential, inaugurated a clock-making establishment of his own.

John Houghton had no sons and when William Frederick Evans (who was following his father's footsteps as a military tailor) wished to marry Houghton's daughter, Sarah, permission was given only on condition that he learnt the clock trade. It is obvious that Evans must have learnt the trade with great aptitude. In 1850, from his original Scott Memorial design, Evans' thoughts turned to producing skeleton clocks on a commercial basis, of a plainer, simpler, and cheaper pattern but incorporating the Memorial replica. He travelled the country selling them while his wife, Sarah, was left in charge of the factory. The Scott skeleton clock became highly popular in Scotland and Sarah, being overwhelmed with orders, had to send for Evans to come home to help with production.

The Evans had a large house, adjoining the factory, where three or four apprentices lived in. Whenever Evans was away soliciting orders, his wife personally weighed out the metal each day. Being a clockmaker's wife was no easy task. Mrs. Evans reared nine children, and died at the early age of 42 in 1860.

Scott Memorial clock

The original Scott Memorial skeleton clock designed by Evans, is reputed to be the only one of its kind. It is shown in Fig. 3-2. It was exhibited at the Great Exhibition of 1851 where he had a stand and, when the exhibition closed, was presented to the retiring Postmaster at Handsworth, after whose death Evans purchased the clock.

When Evans himself died, the clock passed to his son, William Frederick Evans, who died in his early fifties. Again the clock passed to a son, yet another William Frederick Evans, and finally reached the possession of his daughter, Miss Phyllis B. Evans, who is still living at Handsworth Wood, Birmingham, and is the last of the line. Miss Evans, being a great-great-grand-daughter and a direct descendant of the original designer, felt that the clock deserved a place of honour, and presented it to the City Museum and Art Gallery, Department of Science and Industry, Birmingham, where it is now shown to the public.

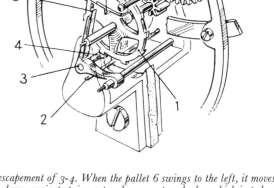

Detent escapement of 3-4. When the pallet 6 swings to the left, it moves detent 3 down against spring 2 to release escape-wheel 1 which impulses the pendulum by impulse pallet 7. On the return swing there is no impulse because of passing spring 5

The framework is of cast brass. The pilaster buttresses, together with projecting gargoyles, surmounted by ornamental pinnacles, are of outstanding quality. Having their own workshop for castings and forgings was of great advantage to the firm, who turned out excellent cast models of Scott and his reclining dog, all of which, including the frame, are gilt. The striking clock movement goes for eight days, is 16 by 24 inches and stands two feet high. It is fusee wound and has a large lever escapement. The large regulator index can clearly be seen (the arc near the top in Fig. 3-2). The platform escapement is fitted in front of the parapeted tower, and the striking is on a wire gong. The movement is seated on an unusual white marble base with a capstan-like pillar at each corner.

Detent escapement

The year 1860 saw the introduction of the detached detent escapement skeleton clock which was produced in considerable numbers. These clocks were made in various forms, particularly at the Evans Soho Factory at Handsworth, Birmingham. The mechanism of a typical detent escapement employed is shown in Figs. 3-3, 3-4, and 3-5. The clock is owned by J. Parry Morton, B.Sc., of Cardiff.

The clock was unique inasmuch as the whole train was inverted in relation to the frame. The detached detent and escape-wheel of ten teeth are separately double cocked together on the back frame, and are geared to an intermediate wheel of the main train.

Beneath the escape-wheel is a detached detent which keeps the wheel locked. Fixed either to the pendulum rod or the inside boss of the crutch is a single half round steel impulse pallet which is given a push by a tooth of the escape-wheel at each alternate swing of the pendulum, chronometer wise. On the following swing the pallet rides over the locked wheel, receiving no impulse because of the passing spring. Although the pendulum registers a beat of half seconds, it records full seconds on the seconds dial. A steel impulse pin or pallet is fixed to the inside boss of the crutch. It also gives an excellent view of the double-cocked escapement.

From Fig. 3-5 it can be seen that the inverted train was primarily designed and planted vertically to prevent any fouling of the chain with the rest of the mechanism. The stresses and strains must have snapped many a weak link on the chain and brought grief to the owner, leaving nasty score marks on the barrel which, all too frequently, fusee chains are apt to produce when they break. The maintaining power click is conspicuous, owing to its elevated position.

A clock with the same form of detent escapement is shown in Fig. 2-16 in the previous chapter.

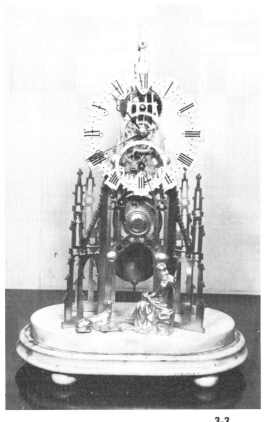

3-3

3-4

3-5

3-3, 3-4, *and* **3-5** *Scott's memorial clock by Evans of Birmingham*

3-6 *William Frederick Evans*

3-6

During the same period, the Evans factory added another variation of this detached detent escapement for a different use. The skeleton frames were discarded and a return was made to the conventional square, or rectangular, plates. These movements were housed in ordinary wooden cases, and were usually supported by round, or fluted brass pillars to give height, a virtue the skeleton clock had because of its design. At the back, inside the top half of the wooden case, a three-piece mirror, two sides of which were angled (copied from the Austrian pillar clocks), reflected the working escapement. The movement did not have the fine finish of their skeleton counterparts and were obviously made for a less affluent market.

Evans is seen in Fig. 3-6 and in Fig. 3-7 sitting amongst his men. The

double-sided business card beautifully embossed, shown in Figs. 3-8 and 3-9, also indicated his business acumen. Use of a skeleton clock as a trade mark demonstrates the importance which he attached to their production. Fig. 3-10 shows the factory.

In the book *The Industries of Birmingham*, a whole page is devoted to the Soho Clock Factory owned by Evans & Son. It reports: 'every description of clock is manufactured here. The lathes and wheel cutting machines are driven by steam power, forging and castings, done on the premises.'

When the clock trade gradually declined, the factory eventually closed in 1935, thus ending a colourful history of over 130 years.

William Frederick Evans died in 1899 at the age of 81 and is buried at Rowington Church, in a small village near Warwick. He left two sons, John Houghton Evans (who set up his own watchmakers' business in Cricklewood, London) and William Frederick Evans, who was in Chicago in the meat business, but returned after his father's death to take charge of the factory.

In an obituary of this son, the firm of William Frederick Evans is described as 'one of the best-known firms of clockmakers in the United Kingdom, which boasts of an existence of over a century and, have secured a world-wide reputation having supplied clocks to towns in Australia, United States of America, Canada, India, South Africa, etc.'

Railway companies were important customers and were supplied with wall regulators. Even today, regulators to be seen at stations in the

3-8 and **3-9** *The trade business card of Evans, which was engraved. Note the Scott's Memorial and another skeleton clock in 3-9*

3-8

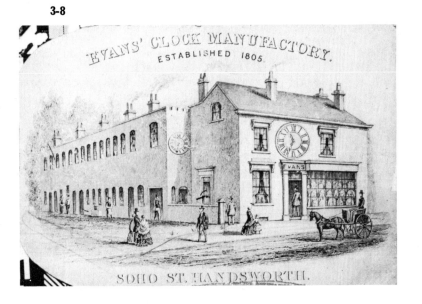

3-9

3-10 *Workmen with Evans outside the front of the Soho Clock Factory. There is a clock display in top window*

remote Highlands of Scotland bear the imprint of the Soho Factory of Handsworth. Another of their productions, the memorial clock to the Rt. Honourable Joseph Chamberlain in Vyse Street, Birmingham, is a fine piece of workmanship and has been highly praised. The Evans factory was the first to introduce and use Harrington's Patent Tubes that one still sees today in longcase chiming clocks.

Evans is recorded in Britten's *Old Clocks and Watches and their Makers*, 5th edition, page 685, as: 'Evans, William, Frederick, Handsworth, died 1899 age 81'. His father-in-law is also recorded in Britten on page 714 as 'Houghton, John, Handsworth, Birmingham, a well-known clock-maker 1797–1842'.

John Houghton retired from the business in 1843 and in 1863 died at the home of his grandson, John Houghton Evans, in Cricklewood.

Edwards of Stourbridge

Another horological personality who had a flair for presenting clock mechanisms in a startling and unique way was James Edwards of Stourbridge, Worcestershire. His version of what was called a large transparent skeleton clock was made of a combination of brass and glass, using flint glass centres to the wheels.

His clocks drew large crowds of sightseers when shown at the Great Exhibition. Although most of his clocks are not marked with his name, their glass centres undoubtedly stamp them as his work. Flint glass was a local product.

In the fine collection of skeleton clocks owned by Major Anthony Heathcote is an early example of this maker's work, seen in Figs. 3-11 and 3-12. An interesting feature of the clock is its flint glass centres to the wheels which have a star or sunray design cut and polished. The design also appears on the lentil pendulum bob, which is also of flint glass. The wheel and teeth were cut in the conventional manner; the brass centre was then removed, leaving a narrow ring or metal rim carrying the teeth. This rim was internally grooved, as in bezels for watches and clocks, and the flint glass centre with ground edge, snapped in.

As can be seen, large brass collets are employed. These are attached to the tapering arbors, the bosses being riveted through the glass centres, on the escape, third, centre, and fusee great wheels. The fusee is detachable from the main frame, having independent screwed cocks front and rear, which are also steady pinned. The fusee cap is steel and is fixed to the top of the fusee cone by two screws.

The wheel diameters and train are as follows: fusee great wheel 6 inches with 120 teeth; centre wheel 4 inches with 64 teeth; third wheel $3\frac{3}{4}$ inches with 64 teeth; escape wheel $3\frac{1}{2}$ inches with 56 teeth. The motion work is enclosed and completely out of view, and is housed in a brass drum. It is screwed to the front frame to which, in turn, is attached the glass opaque dial, the Roman figures being cut out. As with the spot minute indications, all the incisions are filled with gold leaf.

Anchor escapement is employed, the pallets being screwed to the arbor. The clock goes for eight days.

Another unique feature is the isolation of the barrel, which is housed out of sight in a mahogany box in the shape of a cuboid (Fig. 3-13). The barrel contains a three-and-half inch mainspring which is held in a cast iron frame and anchored to the base of the wooden stand (not an easy place for attending to ratchet work). The chain rides through a coin-like slot. Probably the maker realised that the barrel, having to be all brass, would look ugly compared with the delicacy of the remaining structure.

The frame, $\frac{3}{8}$ of an inch in thickness, has the kind of scrollwork design associated with the much earlier thirteenth century. The frame is screwed front and rear, having chamfered collets, and is held by six finely turned tapering pillars. The whole movement is supported and carried by four brass cups. A steel arbor with simple pinion work provides the rise and fall for regulation of the pendulum.

No maker's name appears. There is only an old printed watch label stuck inside the mahogany sliding door, which forms the front side of the

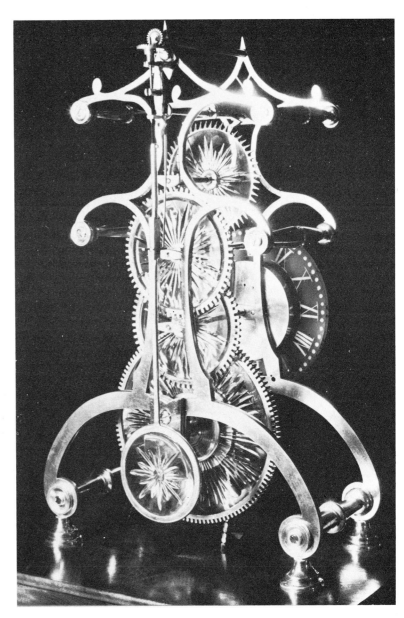

box, and which also gives access to the barrel mechanism. On this appears: 'James Edwards of Stourbridge, watch and clockmaker, Worcs.'

Other transparent clocks

One can see other transparent skeleton clocks bearing the hallmark of Edwards which are similar in construction. These, however, differ only slightly. The fusee is not detachable, as in the clock described, but planted between the framework in the conventional manner. Another small feature are the added twists in the framework scroll design.

These transparent glass clocks were not confined to movements of eight-day duration. According to the reference in the Great Exhibition catalogue, there is a second clock that appears under Edwards' name. Note the wording: '*A new (quarter Day)* spring timepiece made of cut flint glass centres hooped with brass teeth rims, having engraved glass dial plate and pendulum ball, it goes three months and is kept in motion by a new clock movement propellor.'

The old English term *Quarter Day* is applied to the winding sequence for this three-month clock, which is also described as *new*. This clock was, without a doubt, primarily made for the exhibition and fully justifies the conclusion that the flint glass centres must have been Edwards' speciality.

3-13 *Barrel in the base of the flint-glass wheel clock*

3-14 *and* **3-15** *Another flint-glass wheel clock by the same maker, James Edwards of Stourbridge*

It is reasonably certain that every clock of this construction was the work of James Edwards of Stourbridge.

He is shown very briefly in Baillie's *Watchmakers and Clockmakers of the World* as, 'Edwards, James, Stourbridge, *circa* 1795'.

The Town Clerk of Stourbridge provides the following data. 'James Edwards was in business in the High Street, and later in Hagley Road, Stourbridge. He is mentioned in Pigot's Directory 1829–30, Robinson's Directory 1839, Bentley's Directory 1841, and Slater's Directory in 1853, when he was given as being in Hagley Street. He is not mentioned in a directory of the 1860s, so presumably by then he had died or gone out of business.'

A similar version of James Edwards' skeleton clock with flint glass centres to the wheels, is shown in Figs. 3-14 and 3-15. The train system is identical except for the fusee, which, in this specimen, is not detachable from the main train as in the previous clock which is a little earlier in date. Small differences, however, do occur in the frame design, rise and fall, dial, and hand arrangements.

The cuboid base houses a striking mechanism which was installed at a much later date. The lifting piece arm from this mechanism can be seen passing through a slot in the base, pointing towards the fusee cone and eventually reaching to the pin on the minute wheel. The striking portion has a going barrel and winding is effected separately by sliding the panel in the base where the unit is concealed. The striking gives the hours only. Owner of the clock is Mr. Eric H. Mees of Churchill, near Kidderminster.

Liverpool makers

In the 1800s, Liverpool was the focal point for ships from the Far East to discharge their huge cargoes of cotton for the waiting mill towns adjacent to Liverpool. This city's importance to cotton was only equalled by its importance to the horological world. Being a maritime port, it was only natural that it became the centre for chronometer makers.

It therefore comes as no surprise that many famous names in horology have emerged from Liverpool and its environs. Their horological inventiveness had a world-wide reputation. Names that come to mind are John Wyke, Peter Litherland, Isaac Scotson, William Tarleton, Roskell, and Condliff, some of whom have been honoured by having streets named after them.

In spite of the enormous demand for the finer arts of horology, these craftsmen found time to engage in the production of skeleton clocks. The Liverpool-made skeleton clock was partly based on the previous chronometer experience of these craftsmen and partly on their development of the lever escapement. It was James Condliff of Liverpool who created a skeleton clock with greatest individuality. The emphasis in most of his

3-16 *Large balance-wheel at the top of a clock by James Condliff of Liverpool*

45

3-17 *Quarter-striking skeleton by Condliff with lever escapement*

clocks was placed on the huge horizontal balances and helical hair-springs, which became the centre of attraction.

Many manufacturers had introduced platform escapements with limited success. Condliff ignored this method and incorporated his lever escapements in the actual train. The effect of this large horizontal balance and helical hair-spring was to give the impression, from a distance, that a chronometer escapement was being used. The frames were specifically designed to accommodate the large balances, most of them compensated, which together with their large rating nuts, gave the movement a distinguished appearance, particularly when poised at the summit.

In Fig. 3-16 is an early conception of this arrangement. It is a striking clock, the movement being supported on four columns and held down by four screwed brass finials. Of paramount importance are the two barrels containing the mainsprings. These are anchored to the base, away from the main assembly, by two heavy brass-shaped plates, and are screwed to the inside base. The ratchet set up is placed on the rear plate (out of view). Each barrel is fitted with two barrel caps, front and rear. These can be seen cut out in spoked or wheel formation, giving a through view of the mainsprings contained therein.

The base also houses the gong upon which the hours are struck by the inverted hammer. No special reference need be made to the train except that the fusee great wheels have crossings, and maintaining power is used. An excellent view of the escapement is provided, giving a clear outline of the long balance staff, the horizontal balance, the helical hair-spring, rating nuts, and the escapement in general.

The chapter ring is enamelled with Roman numerals, and the clock has centre seconds and a pair of moon-style hands. The front plate, holding the barrels, has been deftly utilised as an escutcheon plate, upon which is inscribed 'James Condliff, Liverpool'. The clock stands 10 inches high, is 8 inches wide, and 3 inches deep, and is dated *circa* 1830. The translation of the Latin inscription is:

'To William Scoreby, a man distinguished for his love of learning, character, piety, a valuer of fleeting time (i.e. one who makes the most of it), and an upright staunch friend. An inhabitant of Liverpool 1833.'

The clock is from the collection of Norman Langmaid of Washington D.C., U.S.A.

Several generations of the Condliff family were engaged in producing skeleton clocks in various forms, which appear to have the original characteristics, retaining the horizontal balance and helical hair-spring. An elaborate specimen shown in Fig. 3-17 is in the possession of the City of Liverpool Museum. It is a splendid example of a finely fretted scrolled frame, having a quarter striking train on eight bells with two alternative sequences of strike, which can be manually selected. The usual subsidiary dials within the main one, denoting strike and silent, change and chimes, have been supplanted by chevron-shaped pieces.

The hour striking is by a gong which is concealed in the wooden base, the wood fret, seen in the rear view of the clock, in Fig. 3-18, allows the sound of the gong to escape. Fig. 3-19 gives a detailed view of the escapement. The horizontal balance is screwed to a collet on the balance arbor, with its impulse pin resting in the pallet fork. Both the pallets and the escape wheel are held at the top by a single cock which is fastened to the frame by two screws.

A curved slot is fashioned in the pallet arm to give clearance from the

and are screwed both front and rear to the fretted frames, the brass collets being undercut. A clear silvered chapter ring has Roman numerals encircling it. The clock has centre seconds.

The elaborate centre escutcheon plate on the front carries the inscription 'James Condliff, Liverpool' with the date '1862'. The two smaller plates read, on the left: 'International' and, on the right: 'Exhibition'. At the rear base of the clock, shown in Fig. 3-18, the inscription reads: 'This clock was made entirely by Thomas Condliff for the late James Condliff'. The movement rests on a finely carved mahogany base.

Another Condliff example

The example illustrated in Fig. 3-20 demonstrates once more the versatility of the Condliff family. This version is a two train quarter striking skeleton clock, striking hours and quarters on three gongs, the gongs, as in most of their clocks, being concealed in a wooden base. The frames are of scrolled design, simple, but magnificently proportioned. A slight difference occurs in the pattern of the frame which carries the horizontal balance. Nevertheless, its grandeur and importance is accented by its placing at the summit.

A close-up in Fig. 3-21 shows the nice placing of the horizontal balance in relation to the frame. The lever escapement, beating seconds, uses jewelled pallets.

What can almost be termed the 'Condliff barrel', with two spoked barrel caps for each barrel (front and rear), is to be found in nearly all the Condliff skeleton clocks. In this particular instance, with the mainspring three parts wound, the light clearly shows through the left-hand barrel against the wall. Both fusee wheels have crossings and, in this case, the fusee chains are blued. There is the fine substantial pillar work that exists in all Condliff clocks, screwed and colleted to both front and rear frames.

In place of the customary silvered engraved fretted brass dial or chapter ring, a glass has been installed to a brass bezel or frame, to which are attached brass dial feet. Upon this dial (seen in Fig. 3-20) the outer chapter ring has Roman gilt numerals on a black ground. The inner ring is white, and bears Arabic figures making up the 24-hour sequence. Both are painted from the back of the glass dial and, after some hundred or so years, are beginning to show some wear in flaking. The central portion of the dial is of clear glass, allowing unhindered vision of the motion work, etc.

The clock has centre seconds hand and maintaining power and goes for eight days. Standing 18 inches high, the movement is screwed to a brass rectangular plate with four ball feet, the whole assembly resting

escape wheel arbor, thus allowing the pallets to swing freely. At the other end of the cock, a screw can be seen projecting from the cut-out portion. This screw is fitted at the opposite end of the pallet arm and acts as the banking pin. The whole escapement is of sturdy construction. Three screws hold the escape wheel to its arbor.

Of special interest is the fact that, in place of a steel escape pinion, a small intermediate wheel has been fitted to engage the contrate wheel. One cannot but admire the position of the horizontal balance elevated in the crown-like frame design.

Each barrel has two barrel caps, front and rear. These are spoked and one can just catch a glimpse of daylight showing through the spring. The baluster pillars are of stout proportions, as befits a clock of this nature,

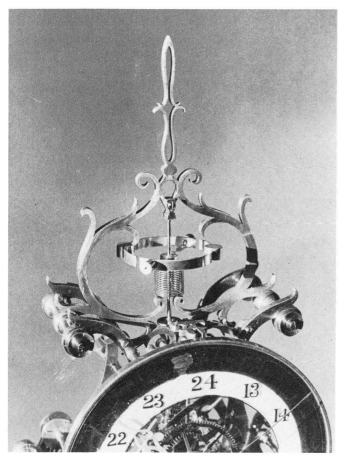

3-21

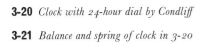

3-20 *Clock with 24-hour dial by Condliff*

3-21 *Balance and spring of clock in 3-20*

3-20

trains. Of special significance is the decorative and magnificently fashioned hour and quarter striking snail, giving a floral effect to the centre of the chapter ring. The two wire-like rods leading to the casket-type base, actuate the hammers by striking the pair of gongs which are concealed therein. The barrel work is of Condliff's design, particularly in the manner in which the barrels are anchored to their bases. The length of the chain running from barrel to fusee is about eight inches, which must cause strain in the chain. One can only conjecture that, the trains being built with absolute precision, as in all Condliff clocks, they run on very weak mainsprings.

A lever escapement is employed. The escape wheel and jewelled pallets are cocked separately by the right angular cock suspended from the frame, whilst the escape arbor runs into the movement proper. The fancy central cock (Fig. 3-22) holds the horizontal balance in position. The balance staff is 6 inches long, the gilt balance-wheel itself having a diameter of 2 inches. A helical hair-spring is attached to the gilt serpent's mouth which acts as a stud.

The clock has maintaining power and goes for eight days. The white-enamelled ring has Roman numerals together with a pair of steel moon hands, and a centre seconds hand. To describe the embellishments set on this clock it is best to quote from Mr. Alan Smith, Keeper of Ceramics and Applied Art at City of Liverpool Museum, who says:

'In general terms we have an interesting collection of decorative motifs which are derived from 18th and early 19th century prototypes. The cupids or "amorina" on the top arch (the centre one is cut off in the picture), and the bust reproduced twice, are quite typically of 18th century character, with long lineage. The pineapple finials occur often on 18th century clocks and other furniture, and indeed on architectural work of the period, particularly gate posts. Lower down on the escapement platform are a very nice group of Empire period motifs.

'The typical sphinxes (introduced through Napoleon's Egyptian campaigns as popular decorative features) and what looks like an Egyptian barge, are on the left hand side. The paw feet and columns are characteristic of the Empire style. The pair of horses and jockeys on the right are emblematic of Liverpool's connection with the Grand National which began in 1839. Interesting enough are the stag and elephant; these can be traced and seen again and again on Liverpool Herculaneum pottery prints of the same era as the clock.'

The wooden casket-like base, with its magnificent carvings, makes a fitting stand upon which the whole assembly can rest. The clock is 13½ inches high, 10¾ inches wide, and 4½ inches deep. It is dated *circa* 1840 and is from the collection of Norman Langmaid of Washington D.C., U.S.A.

A brief history of the Condliff family gives James Condliff at Gerrard Street, Circus Street, and Fraser Street, Liverpool, from 1813 to 1831, and Joseph and James Condliff at 21 Clare Street, and Fraser Street, from 1833 to 1844. In 1851 the directory mentions a John B. Condliff,

on a cuboid wooden base with carved feet. The escutcheon plate has the inscription 'James Condliff, Liverpool' and the clock is dated *circa* 1860. It is from the collection of Mr. R. Mc.V. Weston of Reigate, Surrey.

In Continental style

In complete contrast is the Condliff two train quarter striking skeleton clock shown in Fig. 3-22. Was the inspiration for this clock drawn from the late eighteenth and early nineteenth century French and Austrian rococo concept? The escapement formula embodies all the characteristics used by Continental makers, even down to the pineapple finials.

The movement is supported by four ormolu columns. The frames are of rafter construction and semi-circular design, and carry the two

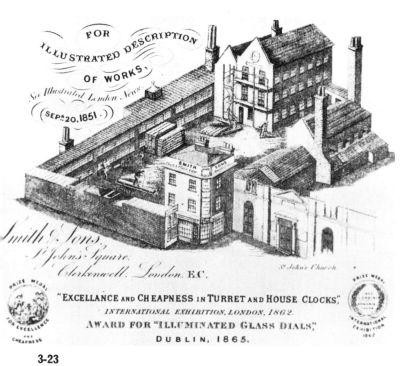

3-23

the most part only two journeymen or apprentices who attend to particular branches of their trade. For instance, the dial enamellers, the hand makers, the pinion maker, the wheel cutter, the fusee cutter, the movement maker, the spring maker, the pendulum and barrel maker, the carver, the case maker, the clock glass maker, the French polisher and finisher, so that when a clock of a particular construction is ordered of one of the masters, he has to depend upon a dozen workmen living in various parts of the district for the several distinctive portions of the work required to complete the clock. Delay after delay is the consequence. "The wheel cutter is so engaged," or "the case maker has deceived me," and such like are the many reasons, and so, disappointing some anxious inventor of some horological improvement.

'It is quite obvious, therefore, that a factory which embraces all the

3-24

who apparently had a dual role as 'clockmaker and beerhouse' at the same address, 72, Gloucester Street, Liverpool. The name Condliff, referring to clockmakers, appears in reference books for various locations in Liverpool, the last being at Fraser Street, under the heading of Condliff and Company, Manufacturers, in 'Watch and Clockmakers' the date being 1918.

Smiths of Clerkenwell

A perusal of the 1865 catalogue of John Smith & Sons of St. John's Square, Clerkenwell, gives further enlightenment on the subject of skeleton clocks. On the introductory page there is an engraving portraying the outside buildings and works of this large manufacturing firm. (Fig. 3-23.) Smiths of Clerkenwell were one of the most important makers of all types of clocks, from the smallest timepieces to the largest turret clocks, amongst which were vast numbers of skeleton clocks.

Some correspondents of the *Illustrated London News* made a day's tour of the works and their comments were published on September 20, 1851. This is an extract:

'There are barely half a dozen clock manufacturers on a large scale, the work being done for the most part by small masters employing for

3-25

3-25 *The turret clock shop*

3-26 *The regulator and general clock shop*

3-27 *The clock-case shop*

(3-24 to 3-27 are from an Illustrated London News of September 20, 1851)

3-27

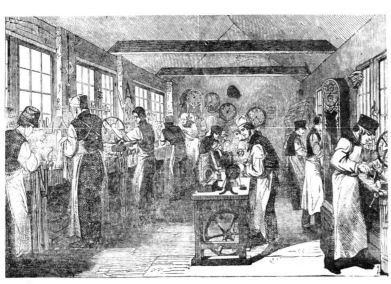

3-26

various branches of the business must possess considerable advantages especially when all the operators are housed under the immediate superintendence and practiced eye of the principals.

'Our attention was lately directed to such an establishment in St. John's Square, Clerkenwell, belonging to John Smith & Sons, which occupies the site of the once famous clock manufactory of Colonel Magniac. One of the principals kindly attended to us during an entire day which we spent in examining closely the various operations necessary in producing a clock, and also several beautiful machines employed in facilitating some of the more tedious processes.'

A lengthy paragraph ensues describing a tour of the part of the factory where wood cases were made, and outlining the many kinds of wood and veneers employed. The journalists then went on to the brass foundry. Of immense interest is their detailed account of the actual casting, from A to Z, part of which continues: 'We find that the sand used for taking the cast was taken from Hampstead Heath, mixed with loam taken from the same locality. All the various pieces of brass required for the construction of a clock could be cast at the same time (see engraving of the brass foundry, Fig. 3-24). The brass finishing shop was for the making of dials, pendulums, forging hammers, brazing, soldering, pullys, repeating work, and wheel-cutting machines. Buhl work of brass and mother o' pearl was produced on a machine called "neddy", clock rings or bezels and turret clocks all around (Fig. 3-25).

'There is one machine in this department which especially attracted our attention, and that is called a fusee engine by which the spiral groove is cut in the solid brass intended for the fusee. The brass is put upon a steel arbor placed between two centres – the operator with his right hand presses a triangular sliding bar, furnished at the end with a steel cutter against the brass, whilst with his left hand he turns a handle in connection with a sliding frame on which is a brass bar, placed at a given angle, so as to regulate the size of the spiral groove. This bar is adjusted by means of a segment at either end. By this machine the grooves of the fusee, of from three quarters of an inch to the largest size required, are readily cut.'

A view of the regulator and general clock shop is given in Fig. 3-26.

The reporters describe at some length the turret work manufacture and finishes.

'After visiting the various manufacturing departments of the establishment, we were finally conducted to the showrooms which contain an extensive assortment of eight-day skeleton clocks representing various ecclesiastical edifices. Some striking the hours on a cathedral-toned gong and others chiming the quarters on eight bells. Then there are oak, mahogany, and rosewood, both carved and plain, many of elaborate designs, and all produced by this establishment. (Fig. 3-27.)

'Nor are these clocks solely for the English market but also for China, Turkey, and other parts of the world, as we discovered by the curious characters on the dials, answering to our numerals.'

The four engravings showing the brass foundry regulator and general clock shop, the turret clock shop, and the clock case shop, give a wonderful impression of diligent craftsmen, some in top hats, working at their individual tasks.

Amongst the stupendous range of clocks illustrated in the Smith's catalogue of 1865, are nine skeleton clocks which are reproduced in Figs. 3-28 to 3-36.

It also appears that the factory embarked upon various qualities in their manufacture which can be seen in their price list (page 56) and that four grades were planned: (1) common; (2) common which were guaranteed; (3) second quality; (4) best. It is therefore encouraging to those owning skeleton clocks manufactured by this establishment to know that skeleton clocks were listed under the fourth classification.

Each skeleton clock was sold complete with its shade and marble base, the price being inclusive of these items. It is with some amazement that one reads the prices today.

One can understand easily the popularity of both the ordinary timepieces and the one-at-the-hour strike, owing to the extremely low price range. Smiths were ingenious in adapting their models. There were three, for example in the form of Lichfield Cathedral. Fig. 3-31 shows one in best quality for only £9.

Drawings in the catalogue tally favourably with the actual clocks. The drawing in Fig. 3-29 illustrates a one-at-the-hour strike timepiece, whilst in Figs. 3-38 and 3-39 are the front and rear views of an actual clock. Fig. 3-37 shows an early striking clock by J. Smith and Sons representing York Minster, c. 1825–30. Notable is the use of spoked-out barrel caps, seen front and rear. On the dial is the name 'J. Dyer, Thame'. The clock is in the collection of J. Parry Morton, of Cardiff, who visited Thame but could find no trace of J. Dyer.

The drawing in Fig. 3-35 particularly defines the knights in armour positioned in the frame niches, and the clock in Fig. 3-40 is almost exactly the same. This clock, which was one of those exhibited by Smiths at the Great Exhibition, now rests in their board room.

An earlier Smiths' version of Lichfield Cathedral, seen in Fig. 3-41, was simplicity itself, having only the essential framework with few Gothic adornments. The movement is fitted to a brass rectangular plate, a lever platform escapement is embodied, and the clock stands on a cuboid mahogany case. The dial bears the name 'Green of Wigan'. The clock goes for eight days and is dated circa 1840–50.

It is obvious that the clocks illustrated in this particular catalogue were only a small proportion of Smiths' major output. Only a brief reference is made to their skeleton quarter chiming clocks, striking on eight bells with hour gong, which apparently ranged in price from £25 upwards. Records show, however, that three month and four hundred day fusee-wound skeleton clocks were also produced by this firm, these particular clocks being mentioned or shown at the Great Exhibition, and also in the Illustrated London News Supplement of 1851.

Referring once again to the price catalogue, the best quality timepiece could be had for only £2 10s. For an extra 15s one could obtain a one-at-the-hour strike, but, to acquire this with a Gothic design, as seen in Fig. 3-30, one would have to pay £3 10s. For these princely sums, the clock came complete with base and glass shade.

There was, however, a startling rise in price for quarter striking skeleton clocks. Business caution is obvious by the addition of the word 'upwards', following the price quotation of £20.

Of the clocks depicted and confirmed as having been manufactured by

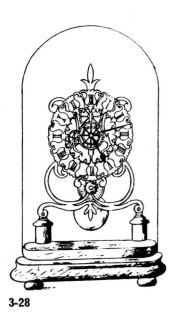

3-28

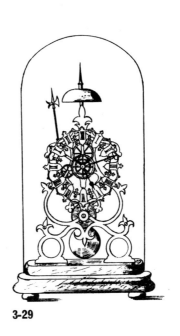

3-29

3-30

3-31

Illustrations from Smith and Sons
catalogue of *1865*

3-32

3-33

3-34

3-35

3-36

SMITH & SONS,

ST. JOHN'S SQUARE (next St. John's Church), CLERKENWELL,

LONDON, E.C.

8-Day Skeleton Clocks and Timepieces, with Shades and Marble Stands complete.	Common.	Warranted.	2nd Quality.	Best.
	£ s. d.	£ s. d.	£ s. d.	£ s. d.
No. 160.—Scroll pattern	... ...	... ...	... ...	2 10 0
„ 184.—New ditto, strike One	... ...	... ...	... ...	3 5 0
New Gothic, strike One	... ...	... ...	... ...	3 10 0
Ditto ditto, Timepiece	... ...	... ...	... ...	3 0 0
„ 222.—Lion and Eagles gilt	... ...	... ...	... ...	6 0 0
„ 188.—Lichfield Cathedral, strikes on gong	... ...	... ...	... ...	9 0 0

All the above with Chains and Marble Stands.

No. 230.—York Minster, strikes half-hours on bell and hours on gong ...... £10 to £12.
Christ Church, Oxford,   ditto   ditto   ditto .... £12.
Mediæval Gothic Registered design, half-hours on bell & hours on gong £12.
Chime Skeleton Clocks, quarter-hours on 8 bells & hours on gong, £25 upwards.
Regulators of various designs, in Carved or Plain Cases, from......£10 10s.

Mercurial, Dr. Lardner's, Gridiron, and other Compensating Pendulums.

8-day Weight Clocks, in cases complete, from ....£3 15s.

Nos. 89, 90, 91.—Outside Illuminated Dials for Watchmakers, Railway Stations and Public Buildings, commencing at £25.

NEW AND ELEGANT DESIGNS IN STOCK.

Quarter Clocks in Elaborate Carved Cases, chiming on 4, 8, or 12 Bells, and Striking on Gong.

DETECTOR CLOCKS, £5.

Fillery's Detector Clocks, ½-hour bell, double dials, £7.

GLASS SHADES FOR COVERING & PROTECTING ALL ARTICLES LIABLE TO INJURY BY EXPOSURE.

Shades for Jewellery, with Trays complete, of every description.

MATERIALS.

Brass Work, Clock Springs, Dials and Clock Wheels in Sets, Fusees, Springs, Barrels, Clock Chains, Steel and Iron Work, Gut Lines, Clock Hands, Winders, Keys, and Pendulums. Superfine prepared Watch Oil. Watch Glasses of every description. Mahogany Watch Glass Boxes.

F. PICKBURN, Printer, Bowling Green Lane, Clerkenwell, E.C.

3-37 *Early conception of a York Minster striking clock by J. Smith and Sons*

3-37

3-38

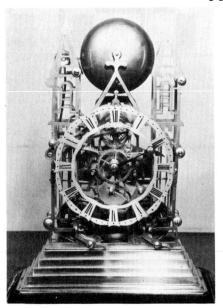

3-38 *and* **3-39** *Skeleton clock which was 184 in the catalogue (see 5-29)*

3-39

3-41 *Lichfield Cathedral clock by Smith and Sons; No. 188 (see 3-31) in the catalogue*

3-40 *One of the clocks exhibited by Smith and Sons at the Great Exhibition of 1851*

Smiths, it is remarkable to note the number which have names appended to them either on the frame, dial or base, many looking quite incongruous, and out of keeping with the general scheme. In many cases these name-plates are screwed just anywhere.

Although the manufacture of clocks has now ceased at John Smith & Sons, they are still a force in industry, being specialist metal stockists and machinists.

Smiths were established in the year 1780 and are still housed on their original site at St. John's Square, Clerkenwell, where even some of the original buildings are still in use.

Trade marks or symbols in every activity have been with us throughout the ages, but in skeleton clock manufacture alas they are practically non-existent. To attempt any documentation of actual makers and their products, would be futile as far as skeleton clocks are concerned. It is worth while introducing one more maker, however.

Haycocks of Ashbourne

Ashbourne in Derbyshire was a noted clock-making centre in bygone days. At various times there were five separate concerns there engaged solely in the manufacture of clocks. The Haycock family came to the

3-42 *Frame patterns from clockmakers Haycock of Ashbourne, Derbyshire*

3-43 *More frame patterns from Haycock*

3-44 *Three Haycock dial patterns*

attached to make up a larger pattern. These are normally screwed to the edges of the main frame at an angle, whilst other pieces could be added to make an even larger clock.

Three of the original dial designs which distinguished the Haycock clocks can be seen from the drawings in Fig. 3-44. These dials were made of brass, fretted out where necessary, and with the numerals added later. They could be either engraved, painted, or superimposed as the occasion demanded, and changed to any model. Looking at the dial drawings, number one – of lacy design – is 6 inches in diameter; number two – with the scalloped-type edges – has a diameter of $6\frac{1}{2}$ inches; whilst the smaller dial, of only $4\frac{1}{2}$ inches diameter has a geometrical pattern.

Fig. 3-45 is an interesting photograph, taken in 1865, showing the Haycock staff employed at the Station Road works, packing some of their products into cases for despatch. They are wearing characteristic headgear of the period, which appears to have been popular in the factories. The longcase clock in the picture is a typical product of the Midlands. The large-spoked heavy wheels being held and lying on the ground are the pulley wheels used to carry the belt drives to the various machinery.

Of relevance to Haycocks and of horological and historical interest, were the machines used for the making of skeleton clocks. On the cessation of the Whitehurst business in Derby, the whole of the equipment was sold. This was originally the famous establishment of the eminent horologist John Whitehurst, F.R.S. Haycocks were able to include amongst their purchases an important fusee engine and wheel-cutting machine, which are still used today when necessity demands. In Fig. 3-46 the wheel-cutting engine can be seen. It has an index plate some $18\frac{1}{2}$ inches in diameter, and has divisions essential for incorporating astronomical work.

The fusee engine (Fig. 3-47) used a lead screw and nut and the pitch of the fusee thread can be altered by shifting the pegs in the holes. This, through a system of levers, works the tool holder. The hand wheel is weighted with a lead rim. There is a square hole in the end of the screw lead to take the fusee square. The cutting tool was fitted into the small square hole in the lever with the projecting handle upon which one pressed down. The profile of the fusee was determined by turning in the lathe, and the tool for cutting the thread was made with a shoulder to limit the depth of penetration.

It was not until the beginning of this century that the Haycocks adopted the trade mark motif embodying dead beat and anchor escapements within the thirty-toothed escape-wheel, illustrated in Fig. 3-48. Although clearly shown on their headed business paper, this device was never used on any of the products manufactured by them,

town about 1816. Two brothers, John and Thomas Haycock, were employed by John Harlow, a clock manufacturer who specialised in pinion making at Smiths Yard, Compton, Ashbourne. Samuel Boulton Harlow, who is shown in Baillie's *Watchmakers and Clockmakers of the World* as the inventor of a ratchet watch key, and published the *Clockmakers Guide to Practical Clockwork* in 1813, was in business in the same town.

In 1826, the Haycock brothers took over the business and ran it under their own name. John Haycock retired, leaving Thomas, together with his two sons (Thomas junior and William) to carry on the business. Shortly afterwards they built new premises in Clifton Lane (now Station Street) and manufactured every kind of clock, from domestic to turret clocks. Their output also included general brass work and iron founding. Among the many types of product to come from this firm were skeleton clocks.

It is extremely fortunate that some of the actual frame patterns used by this company have survived the years. These patterns were exclusive to Haycocks, and thus they provide some clue to the identity of thousands of unnamed skeleton clocks. These original frame patterns are made of brass and are illustrated in Figs. 3-42 and 3-43. Those in Fig. 3-42 were the smaller designs. They show a frame with scroll design, $10\frac{1}{4}$ inches high; one with a floral centre, $12\frac{1}{4}$ inches high; and one only $7\frac{1}{4}$ inches high.

In Fig. 3-43 the frame is of a large Gothic pattern, which is $17\frac{1}{2}$ inches in height. Flanked on either side are the two wing pieces which can be

3-46 *Haycock's wheel cutting engine*

3-47 *Haycock's fusee cutting engine*

WILLIAM HAYCOCK

F. W. HAYCOCK

BRITISH CLOCK MANUFACTURER
FINE GEAR CUTTER

TRADE　　　　　MARK

owing to the fact that the London business houses would not tolerate makers' names or marks, numbers, etc., on any clocks, or clock movements.

Thomas Haycock, senior, died in 1868. This caused a reconstruction of the firm. William left his brother to carry on under the old name of Thomas Haycock & Son (although there was no son). Thomas continued until his death in 1906. Meanwhile, the other brother, William, began business under his own name and, with his own son, Henry, built a new works at Southcliffe, Northeys, Ashbourne.

These works were designed for the large-scale production of clocks for the trade. Within their walls were made many pioneer clock movements for intricate mechanical appliances of various types. William, however, died in 1904. His grandson, Frank Haycock, with his son, Charles William, still carries on the business today under the name of William Haycock. The manufacture of clocks, sad to relate, ceased in 1956, since when production has been turned over to instruments, gearing, and precision parts.

Helical gearing

Clocks with helical gearing always demand special attention. Besides being rare, they are not easy to come by. Attempts to introduce this pattern of gearing by various inventors have had only limited success. The principle has been both praised and condemned and all sorts of claims have been made as to 'who did it first'.

What really emerges is the fact that only one person ever attempted – and with some success – to produce commercially a clock with complete helical gearing and helix pinions.

amongst the townspeople. It is said that here he invented his helix lever (oblique tooth gearing) which can best be described in his own words.

'First it passes equal spaces in equal times at equal distances from the centre of motion; secondly it has a continual line of centres and a single point of contact; thirdly, its pressure is always in a line parallel to its axis by which all friction of the shoulders is avoided and, lastly, it has a rolling action which materially reduces the friction at the point of contact.'

Fig. 3-49 illustrates the MacDowall clock movement No. 149. The frame is of simple cut design, with slender waist. All wheels and pinions of the train are of helix form, the train having a great wheel of 64 teeth; a centre wheel of 32 teeth; a third wheel of 30 teeth, and an escape-wheel of 18 teeth. The clock, however, has the ordinary established motion work, although the wheels themselves are of brass. A thin rim of bronze or gunmetal material has been fitted, from which the helix teeth are cut. There are 25 turns on the fusee, the fusee itself having narrow proportions.

The clock has a dead beat escapement showing a fine pair of caliper pallets with a span of seven teeth. The pallets, together with the crutch, are pivoted between the frames. Therefore no separate pallet cock is employed. The crutch, fashioned from flat brass just over a sixteenth of an inch thick, is unusual in having a slotted curved aperture suspended from a triangular section, and swings between the helix escape pinion (see Fig. 3-50) the crutch fork being fixed at the tongue end of the base.

Slightly altered versions of the crutch are present in other MacDowall helix clocks in which the pattern differs, but the method remains the same. In these variations it can be seen that the centre forms a ring and the extended portion a triangle on which is fitted a crutch pin instead of a fork. Another takes the form of a cut-out triangle hanging from its apex. Whatever the design, they all swing between the helix escape pinion. This is because the whole train is planted dead centre and the crutch included between the frames. The crutch fork, or crutch pin, then protrudes partially through a rectangular slot which is cut out of the rear frame connecting with the pendulum rod. There are end screws or end pieces for the pivots which are throughout the train. The barrel cap is screwed to the inner rim of the barrel which holds a mainspring two-and-a-quarter inches wide. The movement is held together by four turned pillars which are screwed front and back by chamfered screws and are flush to the frames.

The clock shown in Fig. 3-49 goes for one month and has a silvered engraved dial $3\frac{3}{4}$ inches in diameter. There are Roman figures with overgilt bezel of knurled design, and the clock is signed 'C. MacDowall Patent Helix Lever, St. John's, Wakefield, No. 149'. The movement stands $9\frac{3}{4}$ inches high. The pendulum is uncompensated – the pendulum rod being of triangular shape – and has a screw adjustment for beat and for coarse regulation. Fine regulation is carried out from above the suspension spring. The movement is fixed to a rectangular wooden base

Charles MacDowall was born in Pontefract, or Pomfret, Yorkshire, on April 16, 1790, the son of William MacDowall, who had a small watchmaker's shop in Pontefract. Leaving this town, Charles' father moved to Leeds where he continued in business as a watchmaker.

It was hoped that the young Charles would become a chemist. Horology, however, was always his first love. Whilst working in a distillery he ran away from his master, was persuaded to return home, and, in due course, worked for his father, assisting with watches and clocks. Under his father's expert eye, young Charles became extremely clever in this craft, so that when his father died he carried on the business for his mother.

After a time, he settled down and opened a clock establishment in his own right, in Saint John's, Wakefield, where he soon gained fame

and is covered with a glass shade. The clock was originally owned by the family of John James Hall, the well-known horological historian of the late nineteenth century, and is now in the collection of R. K. Foulkes of Richmond, Surrey.

A MacDowall movement presented by Mr. Cooksey of Frome, Somerset, is in the museum of the British Horological Institute (Fig. 3-50). It has engraved on the dial 'MacDowall, Helix Lever, Leeds', and is numbered 248. Was it because of nostalgia for his adolescence in Leeds that MacDowell had the name of this town inscribed on some of his clocks in preference to Wakefield, which in those days was within walking distance – a mere nine miles?

E. B. Denison (Lord Grimthorpe, designer of 'Big Ben') described Charles MacDowall as 'a very ingenious clockmaker but, like many other uneducated inventors, difficult to convince that an independent inventor is not allowed by the world the credit of a first invention unless he is so'. He writes of MacDowall's helix lever wheels as being exhibited at the Great Exhibition of 1851, continuing: 'that another of MacDowall's independent inventions was the helix lever wheels as he called them, but they also appeared in some German clocks at the same exhibition'. In spite of Denison's quips, MacDowall enjoyed the patronage of King George IV's brother, H.R.H. the Duke of Sussex, who, incidentally, was also a patron of horology.

The last fifteen years of MacDowall's life were spent in London where he lived in Jermyn Street, St. James's, dying there at the age of eighty-two. He is buried in the village churchyard at Birchington, Kent.

Fig. 3-51 shows an engraving of Charles MacDowall, taken from the *Horological Journal* dated September 1873, Volume *XVI*, which carries his biography.

3-50 *Helical gearing of MacDowall clock*

CHAPTER 4

DEVELOPMENT OF THE FRENCH SKELETON CLOCK

Clocks as furniture

French clocks played an important part in the interior decoration of homes of the aristocracy. As in English drawing-rooms, they formed the centrepieces on elaborate mantel shelves, or enhanced a corner, standing on a pedestal or bracket.

French horologists were patronised by King Louis XIV himself, and by many members of the court who followed his example. Throughout the second half of the seventeenth century to the end of the eighteenth, they were fortunate in receiving encouragement and assistance from the great artists who were attached to the Court of Versailles. The horologist of this epoch was therefore assured of success, which greatly assisted him in his prolific production. French skeleton clocks were flamboyant, yet the majority were also elegant and magnificently proportioned. Designs ran riot but, unlike those of English skeleton clocks, they were conceived around the movement, which was frequently very ordinary.

Skeleton clocks, like all other styles of French clocks, had to be elegant enough to suit the sumptuous surroundings of the grand salons. Chandeliers, tapestries, pictures, ornate furniture, and ormolu, were the French heritage, and it was necessary for the skeleton clock to match their grandeur.

The period of the skeleton clock was from about 1760 to 1820. Geometrical or rafter design frames prevailed. The clean cut proportions of the frame did not detract from the movement, as did the fretted fussiness of the English skeleton frame.

The French nevertheless indulged in some spectacular tracery, adding lattice-like patterns to their wheelwork, as shown particularly in Figs. 5-37 and 5-38 in the next chapter, leaving no doubt whatsoever as to the country of origin. It is a source of wonder that the fabric stands up to the strains and stresses of the mainspring pressure – again this is typical of all French clockwork of that period, especially in the escapement work, which is extremely light. The same emphasis is apparent throughout both the going and striking trains.

French skeleton clocks were, in the main, made to go for eight, fourteen or thirty days, but a great many went for a year. Most had going barrels for both trains, very few indeed having the English system of fusee work. By not employing fusee work, very large great wheels with numerous teeth had to be introduced to obtain duration. The large wheel in the month clock shown in Fig. 4-2, has over 500 teeth. This clock has a tic-tac, or drum, escapement and only three wheels. The cutting of large wheels was a highly specialised and skilled craft. Great care had to be observed when cutting out the intricate crossing designs from the blanks after the teeth had been cut – this being a feat in itself. In many instances the intricate patterns of the crossings were carried through each wheel in the train, which also included the striking side, as shown in Fig. 5-41.

More often than not, the motion work was left with plain ordinary crossings. Whether these were standard equipment and thought not unworthy to be made specially is mere conjecture. There are, however, exceptions, one of which can be seen in Fig. 5-12, where the pattern is carried right through the train and includes not only the motion work but also the balance-wheel.

All pinion work was of the highest quality and workmanship, was sometimes undercut and had a mirror-like finish which gleamed throughout the movement.

Unlike the English frame, which was fretted into various designs, the bulk of French skeleton framework was simplicity itself. One version consisted of a three arm casting, radiating from the centre of the frame. The main vertical arm, carrying the train of wheels, forms two obtuse angles with the other two arms, and the terminals of the lower arms form

4-1

4-2

4-1 *French skeleton clock with large great wheel*

4-2 *Similar clock with figures*

the supporting legs which rest on the base. It has also been described as an inverted Y, flaring out to a diamond point, as seen in Figs. 4-1 to 4-3, 5-11, and 5-12. Some of the arms are fluted to the centre, others bevelled and burnished to bring out the high-lights. The exact frame pattern was also utilised with a dead flat surface in many clocks.

All frames were mercurially gilt and of fine colour and quality, which can still be seen to this day. The whole assembly is held together by only six screw caps or nuts, three for the front frame and three for the rear. These screwed caps or nuts are made of cast brass and are fashioned into various beautifully executed floral designs, the gilding again being mercurial (see Fig. 4-4).

The Y frame design is common to most French skeleton clocks, and with a few exceptions, did not alter in shape or style during the whole period in which they were made. The particular frame shown in Fig. 4-2 was designed and made by Bernard Gavin Fournier of Paris around 1770 and retained its popularity for a number of years. He was also directly responsible for manufacturing many of the motifs, figures, ornaments, and furnishings which were applied to the marble bases, and employed many artists and sculptors to carry out this work, for which he was renowned.

Ornamentation

The three pictures, Figs. 4-1, 4-2, and 4-3, show varying degrees of ornamentation. The first two have going barrels and the last, which belongs to Mr. J. Lowy of Melbourne, Australia, has a spring barrel and fusee drive.

A break-away from the fluted and bevelled frame, resulting in a dead-flat frame, is shown in Fig. 5-12. Here the delicacy has been sacrificed to provide a robust and sturdy frame of three eighths of an inch in thickness. Frames were also cast in brass with lyre, urn, and floral patterns. The castings were of exceptionally fine quality and workmanship – a task in which the French were unequalled. The majority of these were privately commissioned.

Frames of rafter construction stimulated horologists into creating complex mechanisms. They opened up opportunities for indulging in the layout of intricate calendar work which enabled the many subsidiary dials to be displayed independently. These dials could lead to confusion when amalgamated.

In the use of escapements for skeleton work a great deal depended upon what form the clock was to take. Thus, with a train of three wheels, a tic-tac (or drum) escapement, or a pin-wheel escapement, was widely used. Lepautes' pin-wheel escapement was much favoured by French manufacturers of skeleton clocks, and used only in the finest quality clocks. It was also incorporated in clocks other than skeleton. The pin-wheel escapement is dead beat, with long caliper pallets, which made a good show. The escape-wheel has protruding pins, either in brass or steel (see Fig. 4-3). Bronze and brass wire was first used but was later mainly superseded by steel pins. The protruding pins in most cases are riveted. The escapement has been dealt with adequately in various text books by other writers. I will add just one small note – there was the advantage that if a pin broke or became worn it was simple to replace.

Tic-tac (or drum) escapements were made in considerable numbers. They were cheaper to produce and called for no special comment other than the use of escape-wheels with a large count – sixty or ninety teeth being common-place. There is also a great number of French skeleton clocks with anchor and dead beat escapements.

Clocks controlled by balance and balance-spring had the balance and spring embodied in the train proper, unlike most English clocks which were fitted with platform escapements to their main trains. French skeleton clocks driven in this way had their balance-rims chamfered or bevelled at alternate crossings, which scintillated during its oscillation to and fro.

A remontoire with either spring or weight-driven system, was incorporated in many clocks and in endless variety of design – some spectacular bordering on fantasy, others of subdued simplicity. Examples are shown in Figs. 5-22 and 5-42.

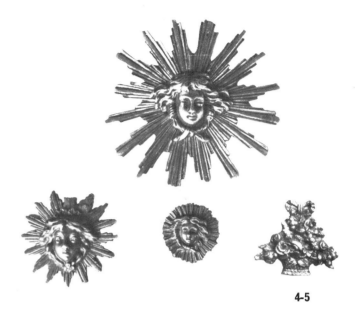

4-4 *Ormolu screw rosette*

4-5 *Various designs of pendulum bob*

Striking sequences provided in the period concerned do not call for any special comment. Quarter striking was sometimes included. The count, or locking-wheel, predominated as seen in Fig. 7-18. All struck on bells, those with rack striking were of a later date somewhere about the beginning of the nineteenth century – as was the introduction of gongs.

Unlike English musical clocks – skeleton or orthodox – French clocks do not incorporate musical trains between either the main plates or frames of the clock movement proper. It was most common for French makers to house the mechanical section separately in the base, which is normally completely hidden from view.

There are, however, exceptions to the rule. The box-like base or casing varied in design and shape, from a plain cuboid to an exotic decorated and embellished casket, which could be fashioned in either wood or metal, the latter being fire gilt. In many instances musical mechanisms were made visible by placing glass appertures at the front and rear. Holes were made on the base or sounding board to allow the music to filter through, the holes being covered over with coloured silk to prevent dust from entering.

The earliest musical mechanisms used by the French were, strangely enough, fusee wound with conventional bell array, employing double hammers. One such mechanism is shown in Fig. 7-17. This was made around 1780. Here the pins on the cylinder or barrel actuate the ham-

mers. Hemispherical bells were used, although rarely, during the Directoire period, while almost unique were glass bells of domed or true bell shape. About the mid-nineteenth century the musical train was produced as a separate unit, complete with bells and hammers. This was attached in an inverted position to the base of the clock movement. Subsequently the bells and hammers were superseded by the ordinary musical box, employing a comb or keyplate. Clocks incorporating this form of mechanism are sometimes incorrectly described as musical clocks.

All ratchet-wheel work for both going and striking trains was saw-toothed.

Of special interest is the very large calendar wheel, looking like an overgrown escape-wheel – always a prominent feature in French clocks. On occasions it was made the centre of attraction by being placed prominently among the subsidiary dials. Calendar mechanisms of all descriptions, from modest dates, to complex perpetual calendars, were produced in many ingenious and intriguing ways, some of which are shown in Figs. 4-13, 5-6, and 5-15.

In French horology, the Directoire and Empire periods were very colourful – particularly in skeleton clocks – when many famous makers contributed to the phase. Most fascinating of all in the skeleton clock field was the introduction of the weight-driven mantel clock (a class in itself) together with the plate glass mantel clock.

Specimens of both are described in the next chapter 'Some French skeleton clocks'.

Pendulums

To the French horologist, pendulums had artistic and ornamental significance as well as function. Since pendulums played such an important part in every variety of French clock it is necessary to examine in further detail their influence on skeleton clocks. Relatively few were balance controlled.

The pendulum rod varied from a steel wire with shepherd's crook for hanging on silk suspension, to the conventional round or flat steel or brass rod, culminating in the Harrison type gridiron, which became almost universal on important clocks.

The Harrison gridiron pendulum developed into an institution with French horologists, and yet, in spite of its special characteristics, became almost stereotyped. Optically it had a special appeal since it gave the impression that it was of significant importance and that it performed some specific purpose other than giving the degree of split-second accuracy for which it was originally designed.

The gridiron pendulum was made of parallel rods of brass and steel which were alternate from the steel centre rod which carried the bob and suspension, the whole assembly being fitted into a crossframe of sustaining bars or blocks of rectangular shape, mostly fashioned in brass.

Both the top and bottom bars are partially drilled, thus holding the rod terminals, and firmly maintaining a parallel position. These are locked by a screw or rivet, through the block to the centre rod. To maintain rigidity, a third or even a fourth bar is added, through which all rods pass. These extra bars have no strategic position. It will often be found that the rods cannot be taken away from the frame or block – because each end of every rod (with the exception of the centre one) has been pinned either to the frame or the pendulum bars, and in most cases to both. The rivets at times are extremely difficult to locate owing to their irregular placings. This practice is to be found on most early French gridirons, right up to 1830. Suspension for the gridiron pendulum is found in two forms – steel spring ribbon and knife edge.

Knife-edge suspension

The return to knife-edge suspension by the French was a reversion of the seventeenth- and eighteenth-century method extensively used in English bracket clocks. There is, however, some difference in the French application of the system.

In the English version the back pivot of the verge pallet was left both long enough, and thick enough, to be fashioned into a $\triangledown$, thus giving it a knife-shape edge. This, in turn, fitted into a $\vee$ cut on the pallet cock. The back pallet, having a knife edge, was held in place by a drop piece called the apron. Fanciful designs and engravings were carried out on this brass apron.

The French, however, had two different kinds of knife-edge suspension – ordinary and inverted. Both systems can be seen in many kinds of French clocks; they are not exclusive to skeleton clocks. The inverted system, however, is extremely rare. The ordinary form is a steel wedge or block found on top of the pendulum and fitted in an aperture of the top crossframe, as can be seen in Fig. 5-34. This aperture in the crossframe of the pendulum enables the latter to be placed on to a flat steel piece which is channelled or grooved lengthwise to carry the apex of the knife edge, thus enabling the pendulum to swing to and fro.

The post, block, or bar, protrudes at right angles approximately half to three-quarters of an inch from the top centre of the frame or plate of the movement. It could be either at the front, or back, or even in the centre of the movement according to the way in which the pallet crutch has been designed.

In the inverted system, the knife edge and groove are reversed. The knife edge is fitted to the post or bar, again at right angles to the centre top of the movement. The channelled or grooved steel plate is fitted in the aperture of the crossframe situated at the top of the pendulum.

The fork of the pallet crutch in all gridiron pendulums is placed between the centre rod carrying the bob.

Quite a number of skeleton clocks have double knife-edge suspension. There are two knife edges in tandem.

Based on the same principle is a similar arrangement known as pivot suspension. In place of the knife edge, two round steel pieces are fitted to a bar, the free ends of these being fashioned into conical pivots. Both points or pivots swing in cups made from agate, cornelian or polished steel. The two steel pieces are adjustable and can be taken apart to facilitate the sharpening of the points. Figs. 5-4 and 5-5 show this principle to advantage.

The action of knife-edge suspension is exactly the same as that which can be seen daily on the pair of beam scales still seen in many shops. Pendulum bobs for the gridiron were solid, and were expensive to produce, as they were heavy and made of solid brass or brass-covered lead of exceptional quality. They were of plain, lenticular shape and devoid of any decoration. Towards the end of the eighteenth and the beginning of the nineteenth century, a hollow shell-like lenticular bob was manufactured and filled with a small amount of lead shot, the bob portion being fitted into a scrolled brass gilt casting of various designs.

On a great number of French skeleton clocks, sunburst, or sunray pendulum bobs predominated in differing styles (Fig. 4-5). To enhance decoration, bobs were fashioned into baskets of flowers, medallions showing French rulers, allegorical figures, etc., all of which were mercurially gilt. A few can be found with choice enamel work showing portrait miniatures or scenic and floral designs. Glass bobs were also lavishly decorated to give an intaglio effect.

Pendule d'Officier dials

Practically all French dialwork, including subsidiary dials, was vitreous enamelled. Some were the work of France's finest enamellers. Most dials took the form of chapter rings or circles and the use of Arabic figures was prevalent, Roman numerals being in the minority. The clock shown in Fig. 4-6 uses Roman numerals in the style known as 'Pendule d'Officier'. Also in the minority were a few special dials made of solid silver, and a number which were gilt. The numerals were superimposed in gold and silver respectively. Such dials were mostly privately commissioned. There was no limit to the choice of exquisitely designed subsidiary dials which produced a colourful sprinkling of moon phases and enamellings of beautiful blue skies and starlight backgrounds.

All main and subsidiary dials were set in very fine matching ormolu bezels, the outside circle, or rim being embellished with magnificently executed chased serpents, cords, ropes, ornate leafage of every kind, and

4-6 *Month clock by Thouverez*

4-8 *Bell in the base of the miniature alarm in 4-7*

flowers – each brilliantly styled and of the finest workmanship. All bases were of superb quality, only the finest of white and coloured marble, and the green-banded mineral malacite, being employed.

The bases came in for much ormolu decoration – floral swags, rosettes, ribbon and medallion strips, trophy and allegorical motifs being added in great profusion, not to speak of the great diversity shown in the ormolu strip beadings which found a place wherever an edge presented itself. Ormolu figures of animals, foliage, and humans, formed complete scenes on the base – again these were immaculately designed and matched, as shown in Fig. 4-2.

The hands were both clearly visible and delicately fashioned. Throughout the years a speciality had been made of picturesque hands, the French setting great value on the use of brass in their manufacture. From this material they were able to create innumerable and intricate arrangements and in this medium they produced a wealth of exquisitely-pierced and chased patterns. Subsequently, brass hands were mercurially gilt. Apart from the hands of the main dial, on clocks with subsidiary dials, the matching of hands was a highly important operation, the same design being carried through each dial.

When steel hands were used, these, by comparison, were distinctly sober in appearance. Moon-style hands predominated to a large extent, but *fleur-de-lis* and arrow-heads had their share.

4-7 *Miniature alarm in the style made for the Great Exhibition*

Miniature skeletons

There appears to have been a break in the production of French skeleton clocks from about 1830 to 1850 when the miniature skeleton clock shown in Fig. 4-7 was produced. It was brought to London and shown at the Great Exhibition in Hyde Park in 1851. It was an immediate success, as can be gauged from the fact that over 10,000 under glass domes were sold during the duration of the exhibition alone.

The basic miniature clocks were timepieces, but many incorporated alarm and striking mechanisms while a more ambitious model had, as an extra, calendar work. Each movement was only 6½ inches high and all were mounted on oval wood bases, the majority of these bases being ebonised. The scissor-shaped frame is engraved on the front, whilst above the 12 numeral, a ratchet wheel device regulates the rise and fall adjustment of the pendulum, which has silk suspension. The bob, incidentally, is also engraved (see Fig. 4-7). A unique feature is that the alarm mechanism is hidden and housed in the wooden base and is wound as in an ordinary pull-repeat, by pulling a cord which can be seen on the right in Figs. 4-7 and 4-8.

A second cord from the main movement (on the left in Fig. 4-7) travels to the base, enabling the user to set the alarm without taking off the glass shade. Each time the cord is pulled, a small pawl engages the ratchet tooth alarm disc, tooth by tooth, until it reached the required setting. The disc can also be set manually, if desired, by removing the glass dome. The clock is in the collection of Lieutenant-Colonel W. Williams of London.

All models had going barrels, with either anchor or dead beat escapements, and were made to go for eight days. The dials were exceedingly plain and took the form of chapter rings or circles. The numerals were clearly marked, mostly with Roman figures, in vitreous enamel. In the centre of the dial the motion work and alarm disc can be seen, together with the steel moon-type hands with the extended tail to the hour hand, indicating the position set for the alarm.

A miniature striking clock with alarm and date was another success for the same factory. In the clock shown in Fig. 4-9, the left-hand dial is used for the alarm setting, the right-hand dial giving the day of the month. In Fig. 4-10 can be seen the alarm train placed at the base of the movement, whilst the going and striking trains are run off the main tandem barrel. A clear view is given of the Brocot escapement (above the 12 of the main dial), together with the thumb-screw rise and fall adjustment on the silk suspension of the pendulum at the very top. The pendulum used is identical to those used in the timepieces.

Turning back to Fig. 4-9, the long curved lifting piece can be seen; it sweeps the length of the frame, the warning piece (out of view) leading into the circle aperture. Incidentally, supplanting the usual notches found on the count-wheel, staggered steel pins are placed at right angles, which are spaced as in the division of a count-wheel to determine the hours and half hours. At the summit of the clock can be seen the eccentric ring or plug for fine depthing adjustments to the escapement.

The movements were usually stamped with a number inside both front and rear frames. Many carry the stamped name of the maker, Victor Athenase, Pierret, Paris, whose workshops were in the rue des Bon Enfants. Incidentally, this maker also invented and manufactured numerous lamp clocks, the rotating globes being marked with hour numerals, the hour being indicated by a fixed pointer. The movements had crown-wheel escapements.

A very small number of the miniature skeleton clocks were bereft of engraving: these were mainly timepieces only. Timepieces were sold for 18s 6d. For those that included alarm mechanism, the cost was 25 shillings. They kept excellent time and can still be found in antique shops. They are much sought after, owing to their compact appearance, and look elegant on a narrow modern mantlepiece. Except for the slight effort made in the mid-1800s when miniature skeleton clocks were introduced, no serious attempt has been made to recapture the glories of the Directoire and Empire periods, with their elegance and breathtaking individual styles.

In a number of French provinces, many independent styles and designs of clocks were created but, except for some isolated cases, no manufactured skeleton clocks arose and Paris therefore became the centre of this art.

In England, however, the opposite situation applied and the inventiveness of skeleton-clock design was not solely confined to the capital, but originated from provincial towns.

4-10 *Movement of miniature alarm in 4-9*

4-11 *Provincial Comtois clock of about 1800*

Provincial clocks

One of the rare French provincial skeleton clocks is shown in Fig. 4-11. This clock is unique inasmuch as it incorporates twin compensated pendulums – a rare feature by any clock standards. In addition, the style of the movement and its method of striking indicate that it is a product of Franch-Comte, where, from the towns of Morbier and Morez, clock production was carried out on a large scale. In general, clocks from this area are termed 'Comtoise clocks'.

Characteristic of them is the striking mechanism, which employs an upright or straight rack, commonly called a 'post rack', by virtue of its rectangular shape.

This particular clock is much earlier than the mass-produced Comtoise clocks. The train is contained in a lantern-shaped frame, with four finely-turned pillars or posts, and incorporates a double anchor, or recoil, escapement with an articulated bar, thus enabling the two pendulums to swing in unison. A fine large skeleton chapter ring can be seen cut into Roman numerals. The clock is unsigned and is dated *circa* 1800. It is from the collection of Dr. S. P. Lehv of New York, U.S.A.

There are some occasions when skeleton clocks, obviously made in France, carry English names and locations. This is due to the fact that a number of clockmakers in England acted as agents for French manufacturers and a few skeleton clocks were included among the many thousands of clocks imported from France. An example is that in Fig. 4-3, which, although French, bears the name 'F. B. Adams, London'.

Shades

Although the clock in Fig. 4-11 has no glass shade, being enclosed in a typical French-styled wood and glass case, it was, of course, normal for French skeleton clocks to be protected by shades. That shown under a shade (not the original) in Fig. 4-12, is a pin-wheel escapement clock with Harrison gridiron pendulum, now in the Franklin Institute in the U.S.A. Both pin-wheel escapement and Harrison pendulum are typical

4-13

of French style. All the hands, which include a calendar hand, are carried on a pipe that projects through the front-hung pendulum which, in this case, is unusual.

Turret-clock style

The French were the first to use horizontal frames for large tower or turret clocks and inspired the form of the Great Clock of Westminster, called 'Big Ben'.

A skeleton clock with a horizontal frame movement similar to large turret clocks is shown in Fig. 4-13. It is engraved, 'Robert, Horloger, Boulevard St. Denis 19, Exposition 1839', and is now in the possession of Mr. R. Mc. V. Weston of Reigate, Surrey.

The clock has a perpetual calendar with three concentric hands with a half-seconds dead beat escapement. There are jewelled pallets and going barrels, and hour and half-hour strike. The all-gilt movement stands on a black marble base, housing the separate calendar work.

4-12

CHAPTER 5

SOME FRENCH SKELETON CLOCKS

Three-month clocks

A very fine quality three-month French striking clock is shown in Fig. 5-1. This clock possesses many unique features and displays a façade of multi-subsidiary dials which rise from an ormolu cuboid base. The overall structure is pyramidical, the main dial being the focal point, above which, and forming its apex, hangs the Harrison type gridiron pendulum.

There are two barrels for the going side and similarly two barrels for the striking train. Above the moon phase dial can be seen the two winding arbor squares of the striking mechanism, whilst the winding arbors of the going train are contained in the main dial.

In Fig. 5-2 the two large-spoked wheels, which partially protrude outside the frame, are the going barrel great wheels. Both can be seen to mesh into a second, or intermediate wheel in the centre. This wheel, and the rest of the train, are separately cocked to the main frame. Whether or not the striking mechanism was an afterthought is purely conjecture. It is applied, however, to the main assembly as a separate unit. The barrel work is conventional. The locking plate or count wheel gives both hour and half hour, striking on a bell. The day-of-the-week star wheel can be seen at the bottom right-hand plinth, upon which the movement rests. On the edge of the front frame (shown in Fig. 5-3) the name Verneuil is engraved, whilst the main dial carries the name Nicol à Paris.

The movement is driven through a dead beat pin-wheel escapement and has a centre seconds hand. The Harrison-type gridiron compensated pendulum is of exceptional interest. It has pivot suspension on two adjustable thumb-screws whose ends have conical pivots for points, upon which the pendulum swings in two cups upon a steel bed. In Fig. 5-4 the positioning of the pendulum suspension on the round brass post can be seen. There are locking nuts (although not in their places) under each thumb-screw which illustrate the clock's superb quality and precision.

There is an indicator showing movement in the pendulum caused by expansion and contraction. It can be seen in Fig. 5-5. Coarse regulation is obtained from raising or lowering the bob and fine regulation from the thumb-screws.

The frame is of rafter construction, and is mercurially gilt. The main dial is silvered and has Roman numerals, with centre seconds indication on the inner rim of the chapter ring (Fig. 5-6). Inside the chapter ring, a fixed dial clearly displays, in French, 53 locations in all parts of the world. As a passing point of interest one may note that London is not included in this comprehensive list.

The central-spoked wheel, or ring, rotates and is divided into twenty-

5-3

5-4

5-2

5-2 *rear and* **5-6** *Dials of the Nicol clock*

5-3 *Name on the plate*

5-4 *and* **5-5** *Pendulum details*

5-5

5-6

four hours, twelve hours of which are marked in Roman numerals, whilst the remainder are in Arabic figures. As these numbers and numerals correspond with the geographical position they give the hour in that area. The moon style hands are of steel. At the base of the movement, four subsidiary dials represent the day of the week, the day of the month, the month of the year, and the four seasons of the year. All are inscribed in French and silvered, the lower centre dial shows the moon phases with markings up to $29\frac{1}{2}$ days.

All dials, including the main dial, are housed in fine quality ormolu bezels. The cuboid base is in ormolu, the finish being left with a matt surface. This is relieved by a swag, held by a pair of cornucopia, the feet and border having a corresponding leaf pattern, burnished to bring out the highlights. The clock is 33 inches high, 11 inches wide, and 5 inches deep. It is covered by a glass shade and dated *circa* 1810.

From the same collection comes the clock shown in Fig. 5-7, a further example of a three-month French skeleton clock. Its extreme simplicity and charm are noteworthy.

The structure has only the bare essentials, but these are of exceptional quality. Again the frame is of rafter construction, the whole being fire gilt. It is a timepiece only but with two going barrels – the two ratchets are held down by cocks, instead of being pinned through the barrel arbor square. The train is planted vertically. A pin-wheel, dead beat escapement is employed. The escape-wheel, about three-quarters of an inch in diameter, can be seen through the seconds dial. Both the chapter ring and seconds dial are enamelled. The bezel in ormolu is finely chased, whilst the moon style hands are made of steel.

The Harrison-type gridiron pendulum is hung in the conventional manner between chops, using steel ribbon spring suspension, attached to the inside of the rear frame. The movement rests on a rectangular marble base and is 24 inches high, 9 inches wide, and 3 inches deep. Inscribed at the base of the dial is the name 'Verneuil Horologer, Mechanicien à Dyon'. The clock is dated *circa* 1820. Both clocks are from the collection of Norman Langmaid of Washington D.C., U.S.A.

Another French Directoire three-month skeleton clock, shown in Figs. 5-8 and 5-9 again illustrates the fine quality and beautifully balanced design which is characteristic of the French. It stands about 27 inches high on its Brescia marble base and embodies a pin-wheel escapement the escape-wheel of 30 pins being mounted directly behind the seconds chapter ring.

The half-seconds, Harrison-type, gridiron pendulum is suspended by steel ribbon spring, the cock protruding from the top of the back plate. Rating can be accomplished roughly with a nut at the top of the pendulum bob, and fine adjustment from a thumb-screw at the spring suspension. There is beat adjustment.

One unique feature of this clock is that *every* arbor is separately mounted at each end in a cock, and nothing is directly mounted in either the front or the rear frame.

The subsidiary dials and the date are: the date on the left, and the month on the right. Poised above the main chapter ring is the moon dial, showing the phases of the moon. The two semi-circles have engraved on them: 'Croissant' and 'Decroissant', the former indicating the increase of the moon and the latter the declining or descending moon. The clock

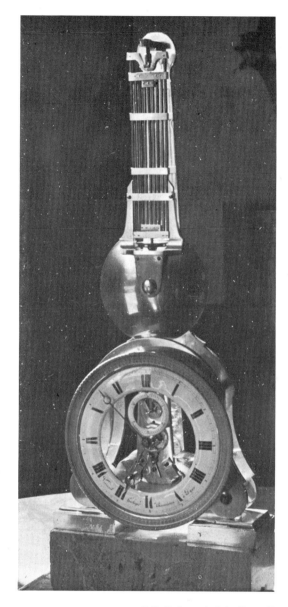

5-7 *Skeleton clock by Verneuil with pendulum above*

5-8 *and* **5-9** *Three-month clock with pendulum above it*

5-10 *Clock that runs for 14 days*

is unsigned and is dated *circa* 1790. It is from the collection of Albert Odmark of Seattle, U.S.A.

Fourteen-day clock

There is a combination of elegance and charm in the unusual French skeleton timepiece in Fig. 5-10, offering the rare opportunity of seeing this type of clock fusee wound instead of with the normal going barrel. The train is planted on the now familiar inverted 'Y' frame with a diamond-shaped summit. The Y portion of the frame is fluted and both frames with their four extended feet, are mercurially gilt. In this instance the floral nuts holding the frame together appear only on the front frame, the rear nuts being quite plain. The eight spokes of the great wheel radiate to the inner rim whilst, on the periphery, one hundred and eighty teeth are cut.

The barrel is anchored to the marble base independently, front and rear, by two triangular gilt plates. Two barrel caps are fitted front and rear with four spokes cut out from each, enabling the mainspring to be viewed, together with its elaborate pierced ratchet set-up wheel.

Above the large centre wheel can be seen a third wheel overlapping the escape-wheel, which has sixty-four teeth, but gears into an intermediate wheel. This wheel is fitted on to the arbor of the escape-wheel and takes the place of a pinion. Fig. 5-11 gives a rear view of this wheel on the escape arbor, and also, the simple and neat design of the great wheel arms radiating from its centre. Silk suspension of the pendulum can also be seen with an 'Adam & Eve effort' at rise and fall.

The clock has an anchor escapement, solid steel pallets, and goes for fourteen days. The plain chapter ring, in white enamel, carries Roman numerals and is clear and well defined, with a pair of gilt cathedral-styled hands, all of which fit into a finely chased ormolu bezel. The decoration to the white marble base, with its beaded surround and motif of acorns and rosettes, coupled with its four ormolu griffins who seemingly keep guard, makes this a particularly pleasant clock.

The clock is unsigned and is dated *circa* 1810. It is from the collection of Major Anthony Heathcote of London.

Seconds balance-wheel

Fig. 5-12 shows a rare French skeleton timepiece with a pin-wheel lever escapement, which is controlled by a large balance-wheel beating

5-12

5-11

5-11 *Rear of 14-day clock in 5-10*

5-12 *Clock with seconds balance wheel*

by finely executed turned lines close to the roots of the teeth. The second wheel, which is parallel to the balance-wheel, is also three inches in diameter. The centre wheel, of four inches diameter, lies behind the chapter ring. Through the centre of this ring may be seen the motion work, the pallets, and the escape-wheel.

The escape-wheel is concentric with the centre wheel and lies behind it. It is separated from the centre wheel by a cock in which run the inner pivots of both the centre and escape pinions. The brass escape-wheel has staggered, round-section pins at right angles on both sides. The escapement is a form of pin-wheel lever.

There is no draw and the pallets are very carefully counterpoised and separately cocked, two cocks with banking pins being employed. The pallet arbor is planted on the line of centres above the pin-wheel. The effective length of the flat steel balance-spring is adjusted by a slider, seen top left of Fig. 5-12, which carries the curb pins.

Although made to go for eight days, the clock, in fact will go for fourteen days. The engraved and silvered chapter ring is severe in contrast to the exquisite delicacy of the clock in general. Its Roman numerals are somewhat pronounced, but are housed in an ormolu bezel decorated in cord and bead design.

The movement stands just under fifteen inches and rests on an angular base of rouge-veined marble, the base being supported by four chased ormolu feet. There is no maker's name to give the clock's origin, but it is dated *circa* 1830–40, and is from the collection of Major Anthony Heathcote, London.

seconds. The train is carried in the typical frame which is shaped like an inverted Y. The frame is sober in the extreme, carrying no embellishments to detract from the delicacy of the working mechanism. The flat surface gives a robust appearance, the frames being unusually thick at just over three-eighths of an inch.

The clock has a going barrel, a common feature in Continental clocks in general. The great wheel is screwed to the barrel which is approximately seven and three-quarters of an inch in diameter. The four crossings, or spokes, seen on each wheel have a semi-circular shaped pattern which is carried right through the whole of the going train, including the motion work, and finally to the balance-wheel.

The balance-wheel is three inches in diameter and has its rim bevelled or chamfered between the feet of the crossings, to give the appearance of being alternately bright and matt, producing an attractive effect when the clock is in motion. The train wheels are further embellished

Remontoire drive

The remontoire calendar skeleton clock shown in Fig. 5-13 is a remarkably conceived and magnificently executed piece. The decoration is reduced practically to four fluted ormolu columns with bases and capitals. The movement rests on a thin openwork base, and is held to the columns by pineapple, terrestrial, and celestial spheres and finials. Through the chapter ring can be seen the pierced rafter frames which leave the movement entirely exposed, thus qualifying the clock as one of the forerunners of the nineteenth-century skeleton clock.

The motive force is drawn from the large barrel containing the mainspring. This barrel does not drive the going train as in normal clocks, but directly drives and operates the striking train, which is placed on top of the movement. Whilst the clock is striking, the spring rewinds the cylindrical weight visible on the left-hand side of the clock, seen descending between the two left-hand columns. This weight alone drives the going train.

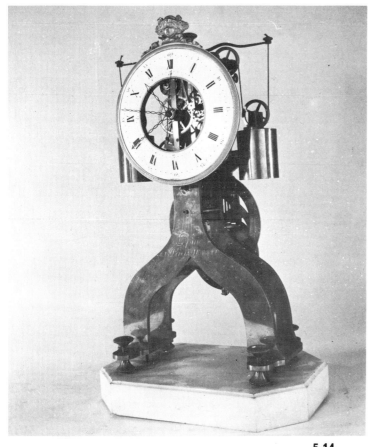

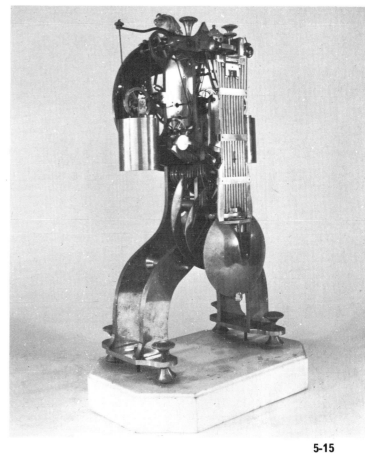

5-14

5-15

5-14 *and* **5-15** *Double weight clock by Lepine*

The clock employs a pin-wheel escapement, the pallet arm hanging down beneath the dial. At its terminal point, a fork projects at right angles, into which a crank-like steel pin (carried on the balance staff), engages. The swinging of the horizontal balance to and fro between the pallet fork, enables impulse to be imparted to the pallets above, engaging the pin-wheel in the train proper. The balance-wheel can be seen on the metal stretcher arrangement placed between the base of the fluted columns. The regulating index is placed on the right.

On the white-enamelled chapter ring, in Arabic figures, appears the maker's signature, Charles Bertrand, and, in the lower portion, the title 'Horloger de l'Academie Royale des Sciences'. The inner rim of the dial is marked for centre seconds. The two subsidiary dials are neatly placed, the left-hand one, in French, giving the day of the week. Through

its centre can be seen (in the clock – it is too faint in the picture) the seven-pointed star-wheel, that turns the day hand. The other dial records the day of the month. All dials are fitted into fine ormolu bezels. The finely chased gilt hands show the French craftsman at his best.

The clock is included here by permission of the Musee du Conservatoire National des Arts-et-Metiers, Paris, to which it was donated by J. Audeoud.

It is customary to find that weight-driven mantel skeleton clocks originate in France and Vienna, contributions from other countries being insignificant. The development of weight-driven skeleton clocks was spectacular rather than horological, and followed the same principles as the movements of clocks previously described, except that they were weight-driven.

Equation clocks

Fig. 5-14 illustrates an important clock by Lepine of Paris, the eminent horologist famed for his complex creations. This is a magnificent

79

5-17

5-16 *Double weight clock with pendulum above*

5-17 *Double weight clock with straight-line train*

5-16

example, with equation mechanism, which shows 'sundial time', by another minute hand.

Fig. 5-15 gives a rear view of this clock, showing the Harrison gridiron pendulum and the double weight arrangements riding over the pulleys. There are four thumb screws at the base to obtain precision levelling.

The clock employs a dead beat escapement which can be seen between the frame openings. The centre seconds are indicated on the inner rim of the enamelled chapter ring which carries Roman numerals and is fitted into an ormolu bezel. The clock goes for eight days, is dated *circa* 1800, and is signed Lepine à Paris, No. 4417. It is the property of Mr. S. P. Lehv, M.D. of New York, U.S.A.

Many of the intricate and complex mechanisms created for skeleton clocks would have been lost to the human eye had the movements been shrouded by a case. The skeleton clock obviously became the medium to demonstrate the finer arts of horology. Such must have been the thoughts

of the unnamed French horologist who produced the splendid weight-driven mantel timepiece shown in Fig. 5-16. Anyone interested in horology will view with excitement the pendulum suspended from the clock's summit. The maker has incorporated a version of Jean Andre Lepaute's compensated pendulum, invented in 1755, in which the temperature compensation can be adjusted manually.

In Baillie's book *Clocks and Watches*, there appears a drawing taken from Lepaute's *Traite d'Horlogerie* which is practically identical to the pendulum adopted in this clock. The pendulum has a long bar of brass and a similar one of steel, which are pivoted to a lever which has an iron bar as its fulcrum and support. The bob is supported on the other end of the lever at a point which can be moved to or from the fulcrum by a screw. The pointer to the curved index, which can just be seen above this assembly, gives temperature readings. The left is marked 'froid' and the right 'chaud'. A fine brass lenticular bob is shown to great advantage, the pendulum being hung by knife-edge suspension.

The clock has a dead beat pin-wheel escapement, goes for thirty days and uses two weights for its motive power. The brass-covered weights are suspended over the two wheel pulleys which can be seen jutting out at right angles. A notable feature is that the brass weights, in their descent, drop into holes, cut out for this purpose to accommodate them, in the marble base.

The rotating calendar wheel in white enamel, indicates the twelve months in French and gives the date and day of the week. The main dial is composed of an enamelled chapter ring with an inset seconds dial. It is fitted into a fine quality chased ormolu bezel, the centre dial plate being gilt. The Roman numerals are very clear and easy to read, and the hands, of moon design, are of steel.

The marble base is light brown in colour with black streaks, its total height, including the base, being 25 inches. It is $11\frac{1}{2}$ inches wide and 5

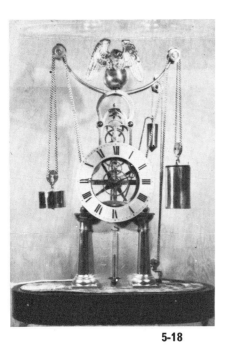

5-18   **5-19**   **5-20**

5-18 *to* **5-20** *Views of an elaborate triple weight clock*

inches deep. The clock is dated *circa* 1800 and is from the collection of Norman Langmaid of Washington, D.C., U.S.A.

A different conception of the same plan can be seen in Fig. 5-17. There is an admirable simplicity about this weight-driven mantel skeleton clock, which also strikes hours and half hours, controlled by a count wheel.

The frame carrying the train is reduced practically to two vertical strips, with the train planted in a straight line. The two weights drive a common barrel by cords.

The Harrison gridiron pendulum has spring suspension, the escapement being pin-wheel. The clock was made in 1817, and was presented to the Musee du Conservatoire National des Arts-et-Metiers, Paris, in 1885 by J. Andeoud.

An elaboration on the same theme is illustrated by the skeleton mantel clock in Fig. 5-18. This clock is a timepiece only, the movement being supported by pillars or columns. The frame is of rafter construction and has at its summit a gilt eagle perched on a silvered ball. At the terminal ends of the semi-circular bracket are the pulleys over which run the chains bearing the weights.

A single weight is used to drive the train, this having a counterpoise, whilst the small bullet-shaped weight is used for maintaining power to keep the clock going while it is being wound.

Fig. 5-19 shows the pulley layout, the positioning of the chains,

ratchet wheel, and the cord at the bottom on the right which, when pulled, winds the clock.

The clock goes for eight days and has an anchor escapement. A thermometer in the centre is on a silvered plate written in English. The chapter ring, which has Roman numerals, is also silvered. The frame and the ornament are in fine ormolu. It is unsigned and is dated *circa* 1810. It stands 19 inches high, 12 inches wide, and is 4 inches deep, and is from the collection of Mr. Norman Langmaid of Washington, D.C., U.S.A.

A similar clock from Major Heathcote's collection in London is shown in Fig. 5-20. Every important detail appears identical except that there is a bezel to the dial, which is smaller than that of the other clock, and the base is different.

Transparent clocks

Sheets of glass were used as an integral part of some skeleton clocks of the French Directoire and Empire periods. The glass comprised the front frame of the clock and the pivots of the wheels ran in bushes in the glass. Three plate glass skeleton clocks are shown in Figs. 5-21, 5-25, and 5-26.

In all plate glass clocks, the bushes or bearings are inserted into pre-prepared holes. Looking at Figs. 5-22 and 5-23 it will be noted that there

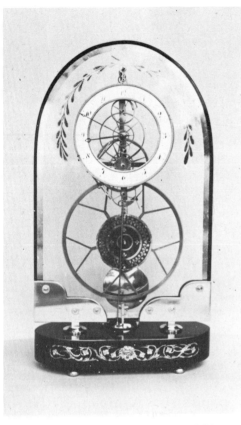

5-21

5-22

5-23

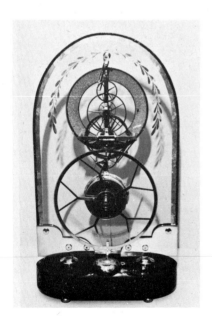

5-24

are three toothed wheels, and a large count or locking wheel, all on the same steel arbor. Three are of equal dimension. The first is the count wheel, nearest the chapter ring, divided into full hours and half hours. The next wheel in the middle, is attached to the back frame strip of a spring remontoire. The third large wheel on this common arbor delivers the power to the centre wheel and motion work. Behind these wheels, a much smaller one gears directly into the large Y spoked wheel fastened to the barrel containing the mainspring.

Thus, as the train runs during the hour, the remontoire spring is wound. This power is then transmitted to the striking train when it is released at each half hour to enable the striking sequences to function. Full striking is therefore obtained with only a single spring. The bell is

5-21 *to* **5-23** *Views of a clock built on a plate of glass*

5-24 *Back of the transparent clock*

5-25 *Spring-driven transparent clock*

5-26 *Double-weight driven transparent clock*

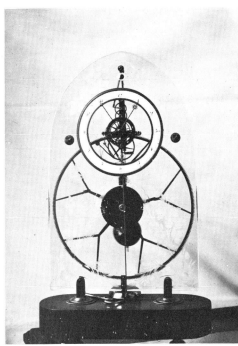

5-25

5-26

placed below the glass plate and a long thin rod coming down supports both bell and hammer, as shown in Fig. 5-24.

All wheels are of high count. For example, the great wheel of the going barrel has 296 teeth. A pin-wheel escapement is incorporated.

The diameter of the escape-wheel is 1·40 of an inch and it carries 60 pins (the correct name for what are usually called teeth). Each pin is approximately 0·011 of an inch in diameter and is spaced about 0·090 of an inch from the next, the drop clearance being exceedingly small. Care must be taken not to damage these pins. A slightly bent pin is sufficient to stop the clock. Pendulum suspension is by knife-edge.

The leaf foliage on the plate glass is engraved. The clock is unsigned, goes for about six weeks, and was formerly in the Ionides collection. It is dated *circa* 1800 and is now in the collection of Mr. Albert Odmark of Seattle, U.S.A.

Another plate glass clock with spring-driven remontoire is shown in Fig. 5-25 by permission of Tardy of Paris. The plate glass frame of this one is gothic and shaped. It strikes also on a bell on the base and is dated about 1800.

Fig. 5-26 shows a different version of the plate glass mantel skeleton clock. This one is weight-driven. The brass bushes, as in the clock previously described, are inserted in the glass frame. In addition to the train, the two spoked pulley-wheels which carry the pair of weights are also pivoted into the glass plate. The movement uses a pin-wheel escapement and is a timepiece only.

The train carries a small number of wheels of a diameter and number of teeth only used in this type of clock. The escape-wheel has 72 pins and a pinion of six leaves. It gears with the large minute wheel, which has 276 teeth, its arbor having a pinion of twelve. This pinion meshes into

5-27

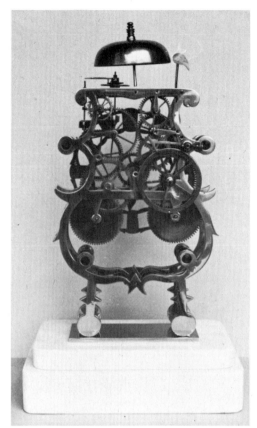

5-28

5-31

5-29

5-27, 5-28, and **5-31** *Skeleton clock with a Debaufre 'chaff cutter' escapement*

5-29 *Debaufre escapement parts*

5-30 *Complete clock parts*

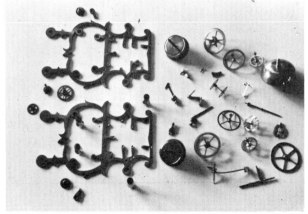

5-30

5-32 *Directoire style clock with glass bells*

the great wheel, which has 320 teeth and turns for some 26 hours and 40 minutes. The arbor of this wheel is the barrel, to which cords are attached. The Y crossings on the great wheel are similar to those in many French clocks. Knife-edge suspension is used. The pendulum rod itself is of steel, and the lenticular bob of brass.

A superb pair of chased gilt hands adorns the chapter ring which has Arabic figures. The ring itself is enclosed in a finely chased ormolu bezel. The floral design of leaves and roses on the plate is an excellent example of the glass engraver's craft.

The clock is unsigned and is dated *circa* 1810. It was donated to the Musee du Conservatoire Nationale des Arts-et-Metiers, Paris, by Mme. Coffard.

English/French style

Figs. 5-27 and 5-28 show an oddity. It looks both un-English and un-French. The cartouche or escutcheon plate near the bottom of the clock would have us believe that it was made by a W. Jackson of London. In fact, a French horologist has cribbed a fretted frame of scroll pattern from the English, complete with fine early baluster pillars.

The clock employs going barrels in place of the English wound fusees. A count wheel or locking plate is incorporated in the striking train, where the English would use a rack system. In this instance, the usual notches found on the count wheel have been replaced by staggered steel pins, fitted at right angles, which determine the hour and half hour sequences. The lifting pieces and their arbors are typically Continental. The fact that a form of Debaufre double wheel escapement is incorporated is positive proof of French origin. The ratchet clickwork is set on the barrel cap, with the ratchets inside the frames on their squares, so that the frames hold them in place.

This escapement by Debaufre was invented in the early eighteenth century. Most textbooks give a full description of its workings, which are unique in some respects. Debaufre's escapement was resurrected and widely used by French horologists from 1800 up to 1875, notably in the manufacture of novelty and so-called 'mystery' clocks. In these clocks, the double escape-wheels had fewer teeth and were made of solid steel without spokes or crossings. They were designed and made for cheapness. On occasions they are called 'star escape-wheels'.

Fig. 5-29 shows the complete escapement parts of the skeleton clock. Some idea of size can be gauged by the balance-wheel, which is 1·4 inches in diameter. The roller carrying the impulse pin is positioned at the base of the balance staff. The two escape-wheels have twenty-one teeth each and are fitted to a single arbor. They can be seen to have five crossings or spokes. The pallets, lying between the escape-wheels, are glass hard. All the escapement parts can be separately removed.

The pivots are conical, their ends shaped as hardened screws with locking nuts (seen projecting from the cocks in Fig. 5-29). The staffs or arbors have pivot holes in the ends to receive the adjustable conical pivots. Fig. 5-30 shows the components of the clock movement. The pallets can be seen in Fig. 5-31 positioned in relation to the escape-wheels together with the projecting cocks fitted at right angles from inside the front frame. Two cocks have been used to carry the pallets, and two for the balance-wheel.

A very English-looking skeletonised, silvered and engraved chapter ring, has been fitted, coupled with a pair of heavy spade hands. It is

5-34 *Swinging pendulum skeleton. The clock is in the pendulum bob*

5-33 *Back of the clock with glass bells*

possible that these may have been the work of W. Jackson of London. The clock goes for eight days and stands on a white marble base. It is dated *circa* 1830 and is from the collection of Mr. Albert L. Odmark of Seattle, Washington, U.S.A.

Glass bells

Figs. 5-32 and 5-33 show an attractive clock with its framework poised on pillar supports. Its fascination is mainly centred on three clear glass bells, shaped like true bells. The setting up of the hammer springs to avoid breaking the bells would obviously be a clockmakers' nightmare, as would the difficulty of bell replacement. In the striking mechanism, the clock embraces a quarter strike 'ting tang', with grand sonnerie.

The arrangement of the clock follows that of large turret or tower clocks, with the wheels in a horizontal line, together with the outside locking plate (count wheel) for the hour striking on the right in the picture, and the quarter snail for controlling the quarter striking on the left.

The one-piece bell standard, looking like a chandelier, is secured by a large finial, the vertical hammer arbors being cocked separately. The movement has a pin-wheel escapement with set-beat arrangements on the pallet arbor, and an Ellicott type of temperature-compensation clearly visible in the middle of the pendulum bob, protected by a glass inset.

The enamelled main dial has Roman numerals, paired by steel moon hands, whilst the seconds dial is placed immediately below. The dial carries the signature C. Detouche à Paris, who was well known in clock-making circles because he was responsible for editing the second edition of *Sauniers Treatise*, a renowned book of instruction. The clock is dated *circa* 1840 and is from the collection of Dr. S. P. Lehv, M.D. of New York, U.S.A.

Swing pendulum clock

Looking at the 'swing pendulum skeleton clock' shown in Fig. 5-34 one is instantly impressed by the absence of ornate embellishments. The clock movement and dial are in the pendulum bob itself and swing with it. The movement embodies a pin-wheel escapement and is a timepiece only.

The thumb-screw, protruding to the right on the lower part of the compensation pendulum rods, is for the operation of the set-beat arrangement, and is connected to the crutch, which is concealed behind. Suspension is by knife edge, the whole assembly swinging to and fro and moving within a very small arc.

The exquisite chapter ring is enamelled and carries the signature of Huguenin à Paris. The bezels, of cord design, are of exceptionally fine quality and are mercurially gilt, as is the matching band surrounding the veined marble base, on which the movement stands.

The clock is 18 inches high, 4 inches wide, and 5 inches deep. Dated *circa* 1810, it is from the collection of Dr. S. P. Lehv of New York.

Historical calendar

For a clock to have both historical and horological connections, is always fascinating. Such is the French skeleton clock shown in Fig. 5-35,

5-35

5-35 *French Revolution calendar clock by Thouverez*

5-36 *The calendar disc*

which was made in 1790 by Louis Thouverez of Paris especially for the Duke of Orleans, who was known as 'Philipe Egalite' because of his liberal tendencies. As leader of the liberals, and a Jacobin, the Duke of Orleans voted for the execution of the King, Louis XVI, who was his cousin. He was guillotined himself in November 1793. His eldest son became King of France, as Louis Philippe, in 1830 and, when later deposed, came to England, where he died. The clock was presumably brought to this country when he was exiled.

The clock has a historical calendar, which operates fifteen times a year, when one item from the table below is made visible through the aperture

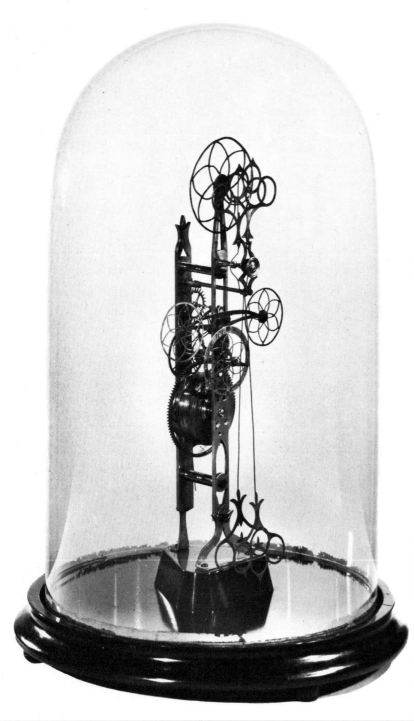

in the semi-circular framework. These events may be seen inscribed on the circular disc shown in Fig. 5-36. They are:

Janvier	1791 le 13	Contributions Mobilieres.
Fevrier	1790 le 13	Supression des Voeux Monastiques.
Fevrier	1790 le 26	Division du Royaume en Departments.
Mars	1790 le 20	Supression de la Ferme Generale.
Avril	1791 le 4	Etablissment du Pantheon Francais.
Mai	1789 le 5	Ouverture des Etats Generaux à Versailles.
Juin	1789 le 17	Constitution de L'Assemblée Nationale.
Juin	1789 le 23	Seance Royale.
Juillet	1789 le 14	Prise de la Bastille.
Aout	1789 le 4	Suppression de la Feodalite et des Privileges.
Aout	1789 le 26	Declaration des Droits de L'Homme.
Septembre	1789 le 14	Acceptation de la Constitution par le Roy.
Octobre	1789 le 5 et le 6	Armee Parisienne à Versailles.
Novembre	1789 le 2	Biens Ecclesiastiques Declares Nationaux.
Decembre	1789 le 14	Constitution des Municipalitées

The frame of the clock is a fine specimen of simple rafter construction five millimetres thick. The great wheel is seven inches in diameter, the spokes or crossings being of Y formation. The clickwork is carried on the barrel cap. The clock has dead beat pin-wheel escapement, with a centre seconds hand. Suspension is by double knife edge and conventional motion work is used.

The hour chapter ring has Roman numerals in the upright manner commonly known as 'Pendule d'Officier'. The two subsidiary dials are choice examples of delicate French enamelling, the left-hand dial giving the months of the year, and the day of the month, whilst the right-hand one indicates the day of the week and the moon's phases. Through these dials can be seen the calendar wheels.

The matching ormolu bezels of cord and bead design are of exceptionally high quality, as are the matching gilt hands. The clock goes for a month and is dated *circa* 1790. Louis Thouverez of Paris is referred to in Baillie's *Watchmakers and Clockmakers of the World*, page 313, as Master, 1788–1825. The clock is from the collection of Major Anthony Heathcote of London.

Scissors pendulums

One can easily understand why the French clock in Fig. 5-37 has been termed a 'scissors clock' because when the clock is in motion the double pendulum conveys this impression. The maker of this clock has resorted to a variation of Dutertre's escapement invented in 1735. In his historical bibliography, G. H. Baillie describes and illustrates Jean Baptiste Dutertre's double pendulum escapement for use in ships at sea.

There are two pallet arbors, each with a single pallet. At the rear portion of each arbor is a small pinion or gear meshing with the other. In front of the movement a single cock holds these arbors in place and on each arbor a pendulum is permanently fixed. The bobs are decorative and skeletonised, as are the counterpoises, which carry a similar motif. The train is contained in a simple strut or post frame. The petalled wheels are also means of decoration. The clock is unsigned and is *circa* 1820.

The clock is in the Henry Ford Museum, Dearborn, Michigan, by whose courtesy the illustration is reproduced.

Spectacular skeleton

Fig. 5-38 is of a really spectacular French clock. The framework is made up of varied patterns of stars, scrolls, circles, etc. The wheel crossings of both going and striking trains are in star formation. Conspicuous too are the remontoire and calendar wheels situated at the top. Both have delicate leaf tracery.

Fig. 5-39 shows the going train and the pin-wheel escapement. The extremely long pallet arms not only span nearly half the escape-wheel, but also seem to straddle the frame bar.

5-39

5-40

5-41

5-39 *to* **5-41** *More views of the complicated remontoire clock in 5-38*

| 5-42 | 5-43 | 5-44 |

5-42 *to* **5-44** *Strange weight remontoire skeleton clock*

The remontoire is operated from the striking train thus, from the very large single barrel, an elaborate arrangement of intermediate wheels (including large and small contrate wheels) winds the spring for the going train, seen at the very top in Fig. 5-40. From this remontoire wheel, the oblique rod in Fig. 5-41 carries a pinion, which meshes into an intermediate wheel to drive the large wheel seen through the opening of the chapter ring aperture. This wheel gears into the third wheel of the going train proper.

The embellishments on both the great wheel and barrel cap have been finely executed. The stopwork can be observed on one of the arms, and through the maze can be seen the locking plate or count wheel looking extremely frail amongst all this decoration.

There is set-beat arrangement and suspension is by knife edge. Fine regulation is obtained from the thumb-screw above the suspension. The calendar wheel records only from one to thirty. The bell is concealed underneath the movement and therefore the striking hammer is inverted. Upon the semi-circular dial placed in a central position above the frame, are the words 'Humidité' and 'Sèchesse' (dampness and dryness).

The whole movement is entirely gilt as are the turned spindles upon which the assembly rests. It stands $14\frac{1}{2}$ inches high and is $8\frac{3}{4}$ inches wide. The clock is unsigned, goes for eight days, and is *circa* 1810. From Mr. Geoffrey H. Bell of Winchester, who supplied the pictures, it is now in the collection of Major Anthony Heathcote, London.

At the other end of the scale decoratively is the constant force escapement clock in Fig. 5-42. The dead beat escapement is driven by the small weight, seen projecting from the side, which is raised by the mainspring every thirty seconds. The fancy remontoire driving-wheel can be seen on the side of the frame in Fig. 5-43.

The clock has a gridiron compensated pendulum and levelling screws on the feet, as can be seen in Fig. 5-44. Beat is self-adjusting, i.e. the pendulum sets itself in beat.

Ting tang quarters are sounded on two bells and the hours on one. There is a calendar and also a centre seconds hand. The clock is dated about 1830 and belongs to Major Anthony Heathcote of London.

'Perpetual motion' clocks

Fig. 5-45 shows a curious French wheel skeleton clock of about 1860 which when in action gives the appearance of a perpetual motion device. The power is furnished by a spring which turns the large wheel with counter-weights on small partly toothed wheels. The weights on the right appear to be the source of power. They are partly rotated by a rack which can be seen at the six o'clock position.

The photograph is reproduced by permission of Monsieur A. Lengelle from Tardy's *Pendule Francais*, 1962 edition.

A similar wheel clock shown in Fig. 5-46, also with twenty-four weights is based upon the same principle. The picture is from Mr. Percy Dawson, London.

5-45 *'Perpetual motion' clock*

5-46 *Another version of a 'perpetual motion' clock*

6-1 *Clock with swinging dial made about 1778 for the Duke of Lorraine and Bar*

CHAPTER 6

COMPLEX SKELETON CLOCKS

Complex clocks in the skeleton formula became so fantastic they must have surprised even the clockmakers. As most are not identified by the maker's name, the antiquarian horologist is often, as with a painting, left to decide whether a specific piece of workmanship should be attributed to a definite maker because it shows something of his flair or style.

Frequently the written reference to a complicated clock is brief. Such a description may be seen on page 335 in Baillie's *Clocks and Watches – An Historical Bibliography*. Under the reference **ca.1790 Sarton, Hubert** he writes 'a clock was made for the Duke of Lorraine with a dial which moves once a minute through one hundred and eighty degrees about a vertical axis and then back, so as to show the time in all directions in a room'.

I found a copy of the booklet in the Ilbert Library at the British Horological Institute in London. The actual description is as follows.

Pendule De Compagnie

Cette Pendule, qui obtint l'approbation de l'Académie Royale des Sciences de Paris, en 1778, comme étant bien exécutée et bien construite pour produire ses effets, fit aussi partie des precieux meubles du cabinet du feu Duc Charles de Lorraine, etc. La pareille se trouve encore actuellement chez l'auteur. Elle a la propriété de montrer l'heure et la minute précises sous plusieurs points de vue et dans différentes places d'un appartement à la fois, en promenant son Cadran horizontalement sur une ligne circulaire et en la décrivant, en trois mouvemens égaux, par moitié de circonférence dans l'espace d'une Minute. Le Cadran s'arrête même pendant quelques Secondes de distance en distance, pour donner la facilité de reconnoître les points indiqués, et ayant décrit le demi-cercle il revient sur la même direction en rétrogradant à pareils intervalles. On peut accélérer ou ralentir sa marche à volonté et l'arrêter par le moyen d'un Poussoir sans rien changer au Mouvement de la Pendule qui va huit jours sans la remonter.

The clock described was originally commissioned by the Duke of Lorraine and Bar in or before 1778, and possesses many interesting and unique features. It could well be the only clock of its kind in existence. It was discovered and eventually purchased many years ago by Mr. Albert Odmark from a Brussels antique dealer, who also described it as a 'pendule campagnie', which appears to denote a clock for a formal room.

The frame of the clock, particularly the rear, can be described as being of rafter construction and having two arms which form obtuse angles to the main assembly, each at approximately 110 degrees, which give a yard-arm effect. Looking from the front arm on the right in Fig. 6-1, one can see it carries the elaborate and crane-like contrivance of the weight-driven remontoire with its attendant runners, lines and pulleys

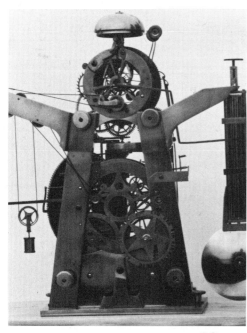

6-2

6-3

6-4

suspending the weights in mid-air. The left arm carries the Harrison gridiron pendulum.

The pendulum is a true Harrison gridiron, i.e. it compensates for temperature change and is not false, and features a knife-edge suspension finely constructed, which is motivated with a Z-shaped link to the crutch and can be described as two right angles in reverse, this piece being some ten inches long. A clear view can be obtained of the channelled groove upon which the knife edge swings projecting from the arm of the frame. Fine regulating adjustment is obtained from the slow motion thumbscrew above the pendulum. The movement has conventional quarter ting tang striking on two bells. The rear view in Fig. 6-2 gives a clear picture of the striking count wheel, showing the hour and quarter divisions.

Extending both to the left, and to the right of the frame one can see the outline of two flys or fans which are cradled in curved shaped cocks, steady-pinned and screwed from inside to form a dial plate. The fly on the left of the picture is to control the rate of striking of the hour and quarter striking train only. It has two blades which can be adjusted for speed control, the arbor terminating in a nearly spherically-shaped worm gear which meshes with an ordinary spur wheel. The hammer mechanism rises from the usual pin-wheel and is carried by extended levers and linkages which transmit the striking motion to the bells.

The clock's present mainsprings are $2\frac{1}{4}$ inches in width, and $1/32$ inch in thickness. It runs for about five and a half days and there are only,

The going side of the clock is run by the remontoire weights pictured on the right in Fig. 6-5. These are wound slightly by about $\frac{1}{8}$ of an inch, once each minute every time the main head swings.

The fly or fan on the right side, also with two blades, is also adjustable for speed control, and provides damping to the remontoire winding arrangement which winds the clock once each minute as the main dial oscillates from one position to another. In taking up these different positions by this particular movement the head 'pumps' back and forth several times whilst the remontoire weights are being wound. This is when the fly or fan is set in motion. The pinion end of the fly meshes with a small contrate wheel which is set between the plates.

The whole assembly – from its central axis, containing the motion work, date calendar, and all the intermediate wheels can be best termed as swinging head assembly. The pinion, working off the contrate wheel from above, about which the swinging of the lower head takes place, is only point one of an inch in diameter. It is therefore extremely small in relation to the rest of the mechanism. Vert great care has to be taken in moving this clock which, weighs some eighty pounds.

There are 722 parts to the mechanism of this monumental clock. Every part – including each screw – is marked in a unique manner and fits only into the one spot to which it has been allocated. All steelwork, screws, clicks, and click springs are blued.

The clock has a dead-beat escapement, the escape-wheel having sixty teeth. The two barrels are anchored independently and are bridged by massive blocks of brass to the marble base. The movement itself is held together by large knurled nuts. The whole of the movement rests on a pleasing two-toned marble base, the lower portion being yellow and the upper grey. The base is $20\frac{1}{4}$ inches wide, while the height of the movement alone – to the top of the bell – is $22\frac{1}{2}$ inches. It is a truly remarkable clock.

That this clock has survived and is cared for is due to Mr. Albert L. Odmark of Seattle, Washington, U.S.A., the present owner of the Sarton Clock, who can just be seen reflected in the pendulum bob of the clock as he photographed it for this book.

'One wheel' longcase clock

Pierre Le Roy is recognised as the inventor of the 'one-wheel' clock. That this invention was regarded as being of great importance is evident when one reads that there were many attempts by other horologists of the same period not only to purloin his ideas, but also to lay claims to being first in the field.

In G. H. Baillie's *Clocks and Watches – An Historical Bibliography*, there are recorded instances, dating from 1752 to 1755, of wide differences of opinion in this controversy. Le Roy retaliated by adding a new striking

on the average, three turns to the winding. The movement is wound by a specially made key which in itself is monstrous, being some $7\frac{1}{2}$ inches across the handle, 8 inches long overall and weighing exactly two pounds (Fig. 6-3).

The upper enamelled dial is a permanent fixture and indicates, on the outer edge, the seconds for the centre seconds hand. The four quarter markings are written in Arabic figures. In the middle band the days of the week are shown and on the inside edge, the months of the year – all inscribed in French. The dial is four inches in diameter and is set in an ormolu bezel. As with most French clocks of high quality, the enamelling and ormolu work is exquisitely finished.

The lower (main) dial shows the time with minute and hour markings – again in Arabic figures. Characteristic of most French clocks, the large star wheel visible in the centre carries the hand recording the date. The date numbers are on the inner edge of the dial. The star wheel is bridged over the hour wheel and has a normal jumper to make it flip over.

The main dial assembly swings once each minute as the remontoire winds, to take up a position approximately sixty degrees each side of the centre, and remains there for one minute. Thus, this dial is alternately orientated first sixty degrees to the right, Fig. 6-4, returns to dead centre and thence sixty degrees to the left, Fig. 6-5, holding each position for one minute. The clock was permanently placed in a salon for occupants to be able to see the time from all directions. The dial can be stopped in one of its positions by means of a button.

6-6 *One-wheel clock by Pierre Le Roy*

6-7 *and* **6-8** *Pendulum suspension details*

6-8

6-6

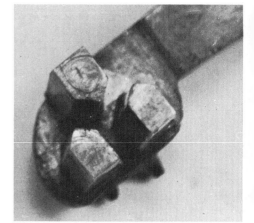

6-7

mechanism (also with one wheel), which he presented to the Academie des Sciences. In the *Mercure de France* of June 1754, Lepaute stated that he had just made a seconds clock with one wheel, quite different from the one made a few years ago in association with Le Roy.

Although the term applied is 'one-wheel', the clock actually consisted of two parts, one escape-wheel being superimposed upon another. The larger escape-wheel has a diameter of $4\frac{3}{16}$ inches whilst the other (riveted to it) is 4 inches in diameter. In rotation they give the appearance of being one wheel. The larger (the outside wheel) has a count of ninety teeth, has five spokes or crossings and is mounted on a steel arbor. The superimposed escape-wheel has the same count of teeth but is shorn of its crossings, except for small fractions near its rim. These metal tongues are riveted to the outer wheel, keeping the teeth clear. The movement is shown in Fig. 6-6.

By an elaborate arrangement the clock virtually has two escapements.

Some $4\frac{1}{2}$ inches above the escape-wheel a set of pallets can be seen engaging a sector-shaped rack (almost at the top of Fig. 6-6). These pallets have a curious cluster formation comprising three segmented steel pieces in the shape of shields. A greatly enlarged illustration of them can be seen in Fig. 6-7. Fig. 6-8 shows the complete pallet unit fitted to

6-9

6-10

the solid steel block from which the double knife-edge suspension is fashioned. The pallets are adjustable and are held by a locking screw.

The sector consists of an arc made of brass which is $2\frac{1}{2}$ inches long and approximately $\frac{3}{32}$ inch wide, upon which are fifteen equally spaced brass pins.

The radii or arms, which are $4\frac{5}{8}$ of an inch rise from a steel arbor. On this arbor there is a hook or claw-like pallet not unlike a gathering pallet; protruding from the left of the arbor is a counterpoise weight (Fig. 6-6).

Suspended from the same arbor is a brass strip carrying at its extreme end a double-arrowed seconds hand, as shown in the view of the clock with its glass dial plate shown in Fig. 6-9. The hand has a loop in it to clear the escape-wheel as can be seen in Fig. 6-6. It also acts as a counter-balance to the sector.

The double escape-wheel is driven by a Huygens endless chain and weight. The chain can be seen in Fig. 6-6, round a small fixed sprocket at the back of the double escape-wheel. As the escape-wheel rotates it moves the sector first one way and then the other. The movement of the sector is controlled by the swinging pendulum.

6-9 *Glass dial of the Le Roy one-wheel clock*

6-10 *The clock in its case*

97

6-11

The pins on the sector enter the W-shaped path between the pallets shown in Fig. 6-7. As they move in constant path, they impulse the pendulum one way then the other. The complete sequence of fifteen pins takes this path through the pallets, then returns. Seconds are therefore indicated on the curved dial at the bottom of Fig. 6-9 from 0 to 30 as the double-arrowed pointer moves from left to right and then from 31 to 60 as it moves from right to left.

The escapement is a form of dead beat duplex. A massive brass cock holds both the escape-wheel and the sector with its rack and counter-weight.

No special comment is called for in relation to the motion work, which is conventional. A single sturdy brass frame of some $\frac{3}{8}$ of an inch in thickness constitutes the main support and has been shaped in the form of an inverted Y.

Double knife-edge suspension is employed for the pendulum, which is itself hung from two steel pieces being of robust proportions (as Fig. 6-8 shows). A steel rod carries the lenticular lead brass-covered bob. The pendulum is slung out of centre.

The clock is wound by pulling the fine brass chain. The ratchet-wheel is fitted at the centre, rear of the frame, this being independent from the main clock mechanism. This ratchet-wheel effectively provides maintaining power. The clock is of eight-day duration.

The oval driving weight of seven pounds has its pulley wheel sunk through the centre of the weight. A steel pin passes through both weight and pulley hole to allow for either the withdrawal or locking of the pulley wheel.

The transparent glass dial in Fig. 6-9, permits the whole mechanism

6-12

to be viewed unhindered, and has gold painted Roman hour numerals. It is held to the main frame by three brass clips. Upon it is inscribed 'Inventee et execute par Le Roy et Fils'. The seconds dial is silvered and engraved at each end with stylised foliage. It is suspended by two brass straps to the main frame.

Fig. 6-10 shows the movement housed in a rectangular walnut and gilt case with moulded borders to the panel, and fluted columns partially gilt to the angles. The panels are glazed both front and sides, the overall height being 6 feet 6 inches, and is *circa* 1775.

Some confusion exists about the origin and maker of this clock. It has

been described in some catalogues and reference works as being designed and made by Jean Henri Lepaute. This is incorrect. Although Lepaute worked in close unison with Pierre Le Roy, Lepaute's idea of a 'one-wheel clock' differs in both his escapement and pendulum layout, although embracing many of the same principles as Le Roy.

Lepaute does refer however, in his 'Traite d'Horologerie' to a 'one-wheel clock' which he presented to Louis XV and that he made it at the suggestion of Pierre Le Roy.

The clock illustrated is from the Ilbert Collection at the British Museum, by the kind permission of whose Trustees the photographs are reproduced.

Epicyclic gearing

'Impracticable', 'badly designed', 'too costly to produce', 'a freak', 'a clockmaker's nightmare' must have been a few of the epithets hurled at the inventor of the scrolled design skeleton clock with epicyclic gearing in the early 1880s, shown in Fig. 6-11.

The inventor was William Strutt, a gifted engineer, whose father, Jedediah Strutt, was a partner of Sir Richard Arkwright, the noted inventor of the spinning frame. William Strutt was born at Belper in Derbyshire in 1756. His parents were cotton mill owners of considerable importance. Very little is known about him except that he was a brilliant mathematician and engineer. Apparently he did not favour writing about his achievements, preferring to act on his own inventions. This is proved in the following quotation from a letter written to Maria Edgeworth on June 21, 1829.

'You ask me for any printed copy or account of my own inventions. Alas, whatever is known of these must have been by other means, for I know not that I ever printed a word about them – I do not defend this, but only as it is easier for me to make two inventions than to write about one, I have indulged my predilections.'

The Chief Librarian of the County Borough of Derby quotes from memoirs in the library which mention William Strutt's inventions amongst other matters.

'In conjunction with Dr. Darwin he availed himself of a rude but original contrivance called a watchman's tell-tale, and so improved upon it as to form the present watch-clock. This machine, though in use above forty years, is now generally becoming known and applied to the service of the public.'

In a further quotation:

'In his cultivation of the sciences, Mr. Strutt was peculiarly distinguished by the ingenuity and the industry which he evinced in applying their principle to some useful purpose. His active and inventive mind was almost constantly at work devising new contrivances which might be serviceable in domestic economy, in public institutions or the arts; or which might conduce the comfort of his own family or friends, to the welfare of the town in which he lived, or to the general advantage of the public . . . the success which attended his efforts in these and many mechanical contrivances, as well as in the superintendence of public improvements of every kind, naturally created a general confidence in his judgement and a deference to his opinion. On the introduction of any new project his sanction was eagerly sought for and, "What does Mr. Strutt think of it?" was a common enquiry.'

A report in the *Derby Mercury* dated January 12, 1831, leaves no doubt about the origin and introduction of the epicyclic clock and its inventor. This read as follows:

'The invention of a machine somewhat similar in external appearance to the sun and planet wheels, which were formerly used in steam engines, and its application to clocks and machines for indicating and registering the revolutions of rotary machinery, was one of his latest efforts and the simplicity, accuracy and complete novelty of his powerful genius and comprehensive mind.'

Strutt undoubtedly enlisted the help of his lifelong friend William Wigston – also a gifted engineer – and gathered inspiration for his epicyclic clock from the rotary machines being manufactured at the Wigston factory. William Wigston was a machine maker, and is listed as such in the first *Derby Directory* of 1828. He manufactured various mechanisms for steam engines, and also gas meters.

The epicyclic skeleton clock, although unique to the horological world, was never seriously expected to supersede conventional time-keepers. The following description of it by Captain W. A. Grant, published in *Watch and Clockmaker* of June, 1936.

'The design is a radical departure from ordinary practice, and epicyclic or 'sun and planets' gear being embodied in the train, which serves the double purpose of gearing up the escape-wheel and at the same time gearing down the hour wheel in a most ingenious manner, without the usual motion wheels for that purpose.

'The centre arbor is driven in the usual way by a spring barrel and fusee. Rigidly fixed to the centre of the face is the 'sun wheel' round which the train revolves. Mounted on the centre arbor, and free to revolve thereon, is the large ring having both internal and external teeth. Securely pinned to the centre arbor, and therefore revolving with it, is an arm with, at one end a wheel and pinion free to revolve concentrically on a pin, and, at the other end, a balance weight. The pinion on the driving arm has eight leaves, gears with, and rolls round, the central sun wheel of sixty-six teeth. The wheel on the driving arm, which has sixty-eight teeth and which is solid with the pinion, gears with the inner teeth of the large ring which number one hundred and forty-four, the resultant acceleration of the ring being four point nine to one.

'The outer teeth of the first ring (one hundred and sixty-eight) drive the escape-wheel pinion of six leaves, and the escape-wheel has thirty-six teeth. The pendulum therefore makes 164·64 vibrations per minute and has a theoretical length of 5·2 inches. The minute hand is carried on the outer end of the centre arbor, a sliding fit. The gearing down of the hour hand is effected as follows: behind the central sun-wheel of sixty-six teeth and concentric with it, is the hour-wheel, of the same diameter but with seventy-two teeth.

'This wheel, which is free to revolve, is mounted on a hollow arbor (which forms a bearing for the centre arbor) and, passing through the sun-wheel and the face, carries the hour hand on its outer end, also a sliding fit, so that both the hands can be moved for setting the clock, but independently of each other. The pinion on the driving arm engages with, and rolls round, both the fixed sun-wheel and the movable hour-wheel, but since the latter has six more teeth than the sun-wheel on an equal circumference, its teeth are slightly closer together, approximately 0·008 inches. The teeth on both wheels are cut with the same cutter, the spaces between the teeth are identical, the difference of pitch being in the thickness of the teeth only.

'It follows that as the driving pinion rolls round both wheels, each successive leaf of the pinion first encounters the next tooth of the hour-wheel which tends to slightly obstruct its progress, but, being freely movable, is pushed out of the way until the leaf gears correctly with both wheels. It is evident, therefore, that in every revolution of the pinion round the sun-wheel it engages the sixty-six teeth of both wheels, and imparts to the hour-wheel a positive forward movement corresponding to its six additional teeth or one-twelfth of its circumference, and the hour hand mounted on its arbor will mark one hour on the dial.'

Only twenty of these epicyclic skeleton clocks were produced. The cost was found to be prohibitive and took up too much time from the main function of the Wigston factory. The first clocks made were signed 'W. Wigston, Derby' (immediately underneath) 'Wm. Strutt, Esqr, Invt', showing this to be a joint effort. A specimen of the signature can be seen in Fig. 6-12 and a full view of the clock with this signature is shown in Fig. 6-11. There are a number of clocks, however, that carry only the signature 'Wm. Strutt'. It is not quite clear when the clocks ceased to be manufactured. William Strutt died in 1830 and William Wigston survived him by only five years.

About 1850, the clocks reappeared in great numbers, manufactured by a D. Bagshaw of London, who follows the Strutt design, but opened out the framework and gave the clock a certain amount of elegance by fitting the movement to a marble base, as shown in Fig. 6-13. The other difference is that the dial bears Roman numerals, and has a skeleton minute ring. The counterpoise to the minute wheel is missing from the original – whether by accident or design one cannot tell. One of these produced in the 1850s may be seen in Fig. 6-14. Although these later clocks were produced commercially, none bore the names of either William Strutt or William Wigston.

A slight difference occurs in the early models, the movement being screwed to an oval brass base with curved perimeter, as shown in Fig. 6-11, whilst the later model has a flat oval base with a knife-edge perimeter.

The numerals were also more pronounced and thicker. All epicyclic clocks of Strutt design are wound from the rear.

Although William Strutt did not seek any honours for his achievements, he was elected a Fellow of the Royal Society on June 26, 1817. He died in Derby on December 30, 1830. He left a widow, three daughters, and a son who was later to become the first Lord Belper.

Spherical clock

We now turn to a rare English spherical clock, which has a fusee and strikes which must be included amongst the complex mechanisms. It is shown in Figs. 6-15 and 6-16.

The circular base is covered with red cherry velvet, from which the clock rises splendidly to a height of 20 inches. The tripod stand and detail ornaments are a particularly lovely colour of mercurial gilding.

The spherical chapter rings are engraved and silvered, the lunar dial at the top is midnight blue, speckled with silver stars and has a three-dimensional moon (Halifax moon) to show the phases (Fig. 6-17). 'Halifax moon' usually describes a rotating sphere or globe of which one half is painted white, and the other half black. Thus, by its rotation, it represents the moon's phases.

6-14 *Epicyclic geared clock very similar to Strutt's*

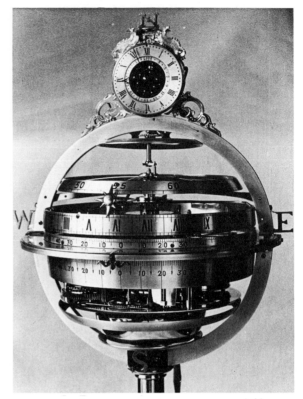

6-16

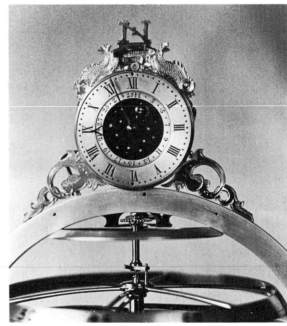

6-17

6-15

6-15 *to* **6-17** *English spherical clock with complex movement*

It was adopted by many Yorkshire makers, particularly in Halifax, although it was not their original concept since the system can be found in the work of many other makers, and in much earlier clocks. In some balloon clocks the 'Halifax moon' can be seen mounted in complete isolation on top of the clock.

A tall narrow glass shade adds a finishing touch to the spherical skeleton clock's appearance. The eight-day fusee-wound two-train movement has circular horizontal frames pierced and snailed for decoration. The arbors are vertical, therefore winding is effected from above the movement. There is maintaining power on the going side. The hours are struck upon a hemispherical bell inverted above the column.

A curious and interesting two-plane escapement is employed, probably to avoid the contrate-wheel. This escapement has divided lift and works very well. The pallet arbor is planted across the wheel.

At the extreme top of the clock (Fig. 6-17) is a perpetual calendar showing the day of the week, the month, and the date, behind which can be seen the intricate mechanism in Fig. 6-18. The dial at the top with Roman numerals shows Greenwich Mean Time, which is repeated on the main chapter rings round the equator.

The centre of the top dial carries the Halifax moon, and also its age up to $29\frac{1}{2}$ days.

A small kidney-shaped piece is fitted at the base of the perpetual calendar mechanisms. One end has been partially fluted, or slotted, out. The whole of the perpetual calendar, together with the recording of the Greenwich Mean Time, is actuated from the minute ring. A boss, which can be seen in Fig. 6-17, at the centre of this six-crossing or spoked minute ring, carries a fixed steel stud, the top portion of the kidney piece, rotating crankwise, thus enabling the wheels of the driving shaft to turn turret fashion, setting in motion the complicated mechanism, both of the perpetual calendar and the remote concentric dial giving Greenwich Mean Time.

On the equator are engraved the names and longitudes of many parts of the world, including the Gulf of Mexico, St. Petersburgh, Canton, the Cape Verde Islands, Turkestan and a great many others, some of which can be seen in Fig. 6-19. An interesting engraving error occurs on the equatorial ring in the spelling of the 'Gulph of Mexico'. The sun-pointer (Fig. 6-19) may be set to read local time at any of these places.

The brass pendulum bob is silvered and spherical and bears an engraved globe, with the names of the five continents. No name appears on this masterpiece. However, a smaller, but virtually identical, skeleton spherical clock bears the name George Jamison, Charing Cross, London, who could be the same George Jamison who was a chronometer maker to the High Commissioner of the Navy, around 1810.

6-18

6-19

6-18 *Back of the moon and calendar work of the spherical clock*

6-19 *The sun pointer is on the left*

6-20 *Skeleton with bar balance*

The dumbell-bar balance thus beats seconds. The escapement is a form of detent, with two separate pallet arms, connected to each and pivoted in brass bushes with steel endplate. The crutch impulses the oscillator by a most complicated linkage. The various levers are counter-poised with screw-adjusted weights.

The clock weight drives a large barrel, which has a diameter of $3\frac{3}{4}$ inches by gut line. The hour hand is replaced by a circular disc which clicks over once every hour to reveal the correct hour in the aperture above.

The minute hand is carried friction tight on a true cannon pinion mounted on the extended centre-wheel arbor. This cannon pinion

6-21 *Clock with bands to indicate time*

The clock was formerly in the collection of Mr. Charles Allix, Seven-oaks, Kent, and is now in that of Mr. Albert Odmark of Seattle, U.S.A. There are similar spherical clocks, but without perpetual calendar, by Jamison, by Barraud (who was a partner of Jamison), and by Henricus Gratte the second. On the latter is inscribed 'invenit et fecit'.

Dumbell balance

The oscillating-bar skeleton portrayed in Fig. 6-20 presents an horological conundrum. The train consists of a great wheel with 192 teeth, of six-inch diameter, a centre wheel with 360 teeth a pinion of six, diameter 10·1 inch and an escape-wheel with thirty teeth a pinion of six, diameter 1·1 inch.

gears with another wheel in a 3·1 ratio, the second wheel having three pins which move the hours in rotation, i.e. this second wheel revolves once in three hours and must have three pins.

The hour disc is operated by a weight which is wound up by means of a pulley actuated by the three pins, and suddenly released at each hour. It was designed to overcome the increasing friction of the jumper-spring which locates the hour disc correctly at the aperture.

The inscription on the dials reads: 'Inventum a Jacobo Wright, quondom Coll, Hert at super Aul. Mag. Oxon, 1826, Jepson, Fecit'. A Thomas Wright patented a form of detent escapement in 1783.

The movement is supported by a tall mahogany pedestal. The driving weight (missing) would have to be doubly suspended, and was probably trebly-suspended in order to obtain any reasonable duration. The fall on a single line would be almost two feet per day. The clock is from the collection of Mr. C. H. Elsom of London.

Band clock

On looking at the skeleton clock in Fig. 6-21, one's first thought is that a terrestrial globe has been removed, leaving just the columns and the horizontal ring. It is in fact a complete clock of undoubtedly unique design. The whole assembly is supported by five columns of solid brass.

6-22 *A normal dial on the side*

6-23 *Calendar dial and worm drive for the crown wheel*

The two vertical hour and minute rings rotate and pass through a rectangular double aperture on an arm screwed to the equatorial ring. The centre, being divided and fashioned into two arrows, positioned left and right, indicates the time. The rings, being friction tight, can be manually altered for setting to time.

The escapement is a dead beat verge and crown-wheel with pendulum and the crown-wheel is at the very top of the clock, being cocked at right angles to the frame. The escape-wheel has sixty teeth, and is used to indicate seconds, the silvered seconds ring being fitted friction-tight over the rim or band of the verge-wheel. At the bottom of the verge arbor in Fig. 6-23 can be seen the helical or worm pinion. This gears directly into the centre wheel. Note how the arbor has been reduced in diameter to provide clearance for the rotating hour and minute vertical rings. The circular rise-and-fall regulator, the size of a two-shilling piece (at the

6-24

On the two vertical rings (seen better in Fig. 6-22) are engraved the hours in Roman numerals and the minutes in Arabic figures.

The stress of the mainspring barrel is taken by the central column and the column immediately to its right, shown in Fig. 6-21. At the top of the central column is screwed a wedge-shaped brass plate acting as a rear frame for the short train which only consists of a fusee, central wheel, and verge-wheel. The immediate right-hand column has been used to carry the fusee-winding arbor (seen protruding through in Fig. 6-21), whilst the barrel arbor enters the same column at a lower level, but does not pass through.

The barrel has two barrel caps, which are spoked out to show the mainspring front and rear. On the opposite side of the clock (seen in Fig. 6-22) from where the central column rises, is a brass plate supporting a silvered chapter ring with Roman numerals, an eight-pointed star inset, and motion work. The clock therefore displays the time by two means.

6-25

top in Fig. 6-24), is graduated and numbered from one to twelve, and regulates the length of the pendulum. A miniature cock is screwed immediately on top of the verge cock, upon which the pendulum is suspended.

The pivoted curve arm on the front column (Fig. 6-22) engages one of the crossing of the hour ring, allowing the arm to change the date on the tooth-ring in Fig. 6-24. A normal jumper is employed.

Four brass urn-shaped finials are used to screw down the equatorial band. Hung from the front column is a plumb line, seen in Fig. 6-22. The clock is levelled by the knurled, finial-styled thumb-screws on the base.

An elliptical brass-engraved plate carries the name 'Jas. Merlin, Inventor, London, 1776'. Jas. Merlin was principal mechanic to James Cox, the celebrated English designer and maker of automata and musical clocks. The clock which runs for eight days is from the collection of Mr. Charles Allix of Bradbourne Farm, Sevenoaks, Kent, and was described and illustrated in *Antiquarian Horology*, June, 1967.

Centrifugal striking

The skeleton clock formula often presents an element of surprise. It is difficult to assess what was in the mind of the creator when accomplishing the horological enigma shown in Fig. 6-25. Not only is it unorthodox by incorporating an inverted going train, but mystifies us by its striking mechanism which is devoid of any train.

There is a single wheel for the strike. The hammer arbor is pinioned at one end and meshes direct into this large wheel, the hammer head being pivoted almost half-way up the rod or shaft. It can be observed at the top of Fig. 6-26 that the pivoted section of the hammer head lies at a right angle. This is kept in position by a weak spring to enable it to provide a quick get-away. Once momentum is attained, the hammer head flies outwards by centrifugal force striking the bell in passing. The gathering pallet is fitted to the opposite pivot end of the arbor. The whole contrivance carries a lead counterpoise weight which hangs from the pinioned arbor.

An unusually extended rack arm has been fashioned to reach the snail, whilst an independent arm acts as a warning piece. Both rack and warning lever (the latter reaching up to the gathering pallet), are pivoted together on one stud or pillar and operate in scissor formation.

The brass frame is of a simple cruciform design, the movement employing an anchor escapement with a compound pendulum, which has a four-seconds beat. Suspension is by knife edge, the steel V-X piece swinging on an agate bed. The pendulum rod carries angular-shaped bobs at top and bottom. Both bobs are made of lead.

The movement is weight-driven and reposes on a pedestal. Fig. 6-27 shows the lines running from both the going train and the single-strike wheel, with the lines running over a pair of brass rollers, which were added by a previous owner as guides to clear the escapement.

Blue paper has been pasted on the back of the skeleton dial, in Fig. 6-25, but has now been removed. There is no name to this English clock, which is *circa* 1850. It is in the collection of Mr. Norman Langmaid, Washington, U.S.A.

6-26

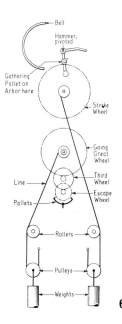

6-27

6-26 *Bell hammer at the top with flail arm*

6-27 *Plan of the movement, from a sketch by the former owner, B. H. Hall of Aldeburgh, who made certain alterations including the addition of rollers*

Thirteen-dial clock

A clock with thirteen dials is certainly a prestige piece. A specimen is shown in Fig. 6-28. The whole mechanism is driven by a single going barrel (the clock being a timepiece). The barrel great wheel meshes to a twelve-leaved pinion which is carried by a large intermediate wheel. Centre and third wheels have pinions of ten, as has also the pin-wheel, this being the form of escapement.

Every pivot, throughout the whole of the train, including those in all the subsidiary dials, is fitted both on the front and rear frames with real garnet endstones. All together there are fifty-four of these jewelled bearings, some of which may be seen on the back of the movement in Fig. 6-29.

The main dial has a fine pair of gilt chased hands and a sweep seconds hand showing half seconds beat. Above the main dial is the equation dial showing mean time and solar time. Mean and solar time agree exactly on only one day of the year.

Immediately below the main dial is the month dial, which also shows the signs of the zodiac, together with the four seasons. To the left of the main dial may be seen the days of the week (in French) coupled with the daily planetary signs, the outer rim giving the days of the month. On the right of the main dial is a small dial showing the phases and the age of the moon.

The eight lower dials are in two-tone enamels, white and midnight blue, each one being marked out for twenty-four hours in Roman numerals.

The numerals in the white zone are black, having the word 'Midi' underneath the twelve o'clock. In the midnight blue zone, the numerals are gold, with the word 'Minuit' above the twelve o'clock. The eight dials record the time in London, New York, St. Petersburgh, Canton, Tahiti, Alexandria, Algiers, and St. Helena.

The angled view from the rear in Fig. 6-29 shows how the escapement is placed. The calendar and moon phase star-wheel mechanisms are turned by rotating pawls. The compensated pendulum has no special features. The carving that surrounds the front of the clock is wood and of fine workmanship.

The movement, signed Emmanuel Esconbe 'fecit' 1856 á Toulouse, goes for one month. It was purchased by a French watchmaker who emigrated to New York as a small boy and, remembering it from his boyhood, had acquired it from the maker's granddaughter in 1937.

He willed it to go either to a museum or a collector and it joined the collection of Mr. Norman Langmaid of Washington, D.C., U.S.A.

6-28

6-29

6-28 *Thirteen dial world-time clock*

6-29 *Back of the multi-dial clock in 6-28*

CHAPTER 7

YEAR CLOCKS, LONGCASE, AND MUSICAL CLOCKS

Year clocks

Ferdinand Berthoud, the eminent French horologist, needs no introduction to collecters. His achievements have left an indelible mark on the history of horology. There is no doubt that his creativeness stemmed from the master he served under, Julien Le Roy. Berthoud's skeleton clock, which runs for a year when wound, is shown in Figs. 7-1 and 7-2.

The frame is of rafter construction and the clock's general shape is that of a handbell made of brass approximately a quarter of an inch thick. The train is as follows: the great wheel of the going barrel has 136 teeth with eight crossings or spokes, the second, or intermediate wheel has 204 teeth driving a pinion of ten (note the radial arms of crossings leading to the fine criss-cross design to the wheel rim). The third wheel carries 210 teeth to a pinion of eight, whilst the fourth wheel has eighty teeth and a pinion of ten, which also drives the motion work of eighty teeth and revolves once an hour (minute hand).

The escape-wheel of the dead beat (pin-wheel escapement has sixty pins); with a pinion of eight. The pallets are adjustable.

Ordinary ribbon steel suspension is used for the Harrison-type gridiron pendulum which has a bi-metallic thermometer in its bob.

A feature of this clock is that once the mainspring is let down and the ratchet work removed, the bridge can be lifted from the frame, thus allowing the going barrel to be pulled away from the main structure.

The clock has centre seconds hand indicating on a white enamelled chapter ring with half-second divisions, and the hour and minute hands are of well-defined moon pattern and under them is a slight scroll decoration. The signature of Ferdinand Berthoud appears on the outer seconds ring above the twelve o'clock. The bezel surrounding the chapter

7-2

ring is of leaf and rope pattern, and, mercurially gilt, just below the dial on the main front frame is the following inscription: 'Pendule allant un an Execute par Ferdinand Berthoud'.

The movement rests on a veined oval green marble base and the clock is dated *circa* 1780. It is from the Ilbert Collection and is included here by kind permission of the Trustees of the British Museum, London.

That other clockmakers should produce skeleton clocks that would go for one year or more at a winding was inevitable. Recorded instances of long-duration skeleton clocks in most cases describe them as going for 400 days. One, however, is stated to go for 500 days, and another reputed to run for three years.

English fusee long-duration clocks, and French multi-barrel year clocks, must not be confused with the modern version of the 400-day clock which has a rotating pendulum with a circular bob under a glass dome and is of German manufacture.

In skeleton clocks of one year's duration or more, the principle of construction is similar to that of all multi-barrel clocks, whether fusee-driven, or with going barrels. French year clocks can employ up to sixteen barrels. One of these is shown in Fig. 7-3. It is what might be called a 'semi-skeleton' and is in the collection of Lord Harris of Belmont Part, Faversham, Kent.

Mr. E. H. Pearsons of Messrs. Pearsons & Sons of Romford, Essex, have a 400-day skeleton clock in their jeweller's shop. It is shown in Fig. 7-4.

The frame is of simple but robust design, being 5/16th inches thick and made of brass. The front frame is six inches shorter than the rear frame, the whole movement being screwed back and front to business-like pillars with blued-steel screws and blued washers.

The clock's special features are that the train consists of four barrels, each containing three-inch mainsprings. There are two fusees and the train is so planted that two barrels are deployed independently for each fusee, which can be seen left and right of the frame between 4 and 5, and 7 and 8. The lower barrel is connected to the upper barrel by a chain, the upper barrel in turn is connected to the fusee by another, but separate, chain. Thus there is a combined force of two mainsprings on the one fusee.

The same procedure is carried out on the opposite side – this is applicable to any other multi-barrel combination using fusee work. The upper barrel is always full of chain since it draws its chain from the fusee, thus replacing that already taken from the barrel.

Each mainspring is set up a half a turn on the ratchet. The ratchet work on this clock was not pinned, neither do any holes appear on the barrel arbors for this purpose. No doubt the designer was confident that the power would retain the clicks in their place, particularly for the lower barrels. Of special interest are the bottom click on the left-hand side, and the top click on the right, which are set to the ratchet in the reverse position and are of different shape from the other two clicks.

Both fusee great wheels mesh into a $\frac{5}{8}$-inch diameter pinion of thirty-two leaves, which is an exceptionally high count for this type of clock and was probably adopted to eliminate undue friction, and reduce the loading per tooth.

This pinion carries the combined force of the four mainsprings, which

7-3

7-2 *Side view of Berthoud's year clock*

7-3 *French multi-barrel year clock*

have a pulling power of 120 pounds or more. There are two intermediate wheels between the fusee and centre-wheel, the train being completed by the usual third and escape-wheels and pallets. The centre, third, and escape-wheels, together with the pallets, are separately cocked. Although these cocks are screwed and steady-pinned, the top bars are so curved and elongated (Fig. 7-5), they could be drawn by the force of the movement, causing the clock to stop. Accurate depthing is therefore essential.

At one stage, as can be seen by the unusual bearing in Fig. 7-5, the centre arbor was carried to the back frame. This obviously was found to be too great a strain and possibly the arbor broke, hence a cock, matching the others, has been incorporated halfway between the frame, using the old arbor and making it much shorter to lessen the bending strain. The clock has anchor escapement and all wheels throughout the movement, including motion work and calendar wheels, have six crossings or spokes.

The calendar date mechanism is carried on a separate miniature skeleton frame with a train of four wheels and is screwed from inside the front main frame. This gears direct from the three-inch intermediate wheel, the pinion of which meshes with both fusee great wheels. The calendar therefore is independent of the motion work. The last wheel carrying the hand recording the date has the appearance of a Brocot-style escape-wheel, the teeth of which are locked by the usual detent or jumper.

The motion work calls for no special mention and is orthodox. As the two fusee winding arbors are reversed, the clock is wound from the back. The dial, as in most skeleton clocks, is made from one piece of sheet brass pierced and silvered, and has Arabic figures with a pair of steel moon-type hands. The clock stands 21 inches high on a brass elliptical base,

7-5

7-4 *400-day clock in a retail jeweller's shop*

7-5 *Three wheels and pallets have separate cocks*

shortened in the previous clock (Fig. 7-5), is carried in this case to the rear frame. The fusee chain is about 1/32 inch wide and 3/16 inch thick.

The subsidiary dial on the left records the weeks of the year. The right-hand dial gives the date. The star wheels and jumper mechanisms can be clearly seen looking at the front of the clock.

The Arabic dial is identical to that of the previous clock with the same fancy decoration which is blacked in on a silvered background.

The clock has an anchor escapement and is wound from the rear. Engraved on its brass base is the name B. Parker, Bury St. Edmunds. It is *circa* 1845–50 and from the collection of Major Anthony Heathcote, London.

Figs. 7-8 and 7-9 show a rare French one-year skeleton clock with a double dial. It is rare because it incorporates a duplex escapement. The escapement is at the summit of the movement, which has a helical free-sprung hair-spring, better seen in Fig. 7-10.

The four going barrels convey the power to maintain the duration for the year and are situated in pairs, the two top barrels meshing into the large wheel in the centre.

The frame, by necessity, is robust and of simple scroll design. The top dial is in the orthodox English regulator tradition. In addition, through the various apertures can be seen the day of the week, the week of the month, the month of the year and the last two digits of the current year.

The lower dial is a world time dial, comprising a fixed twenty-four-hour chapter ring in Roman numerals, on which the inner dial rotates.

7-6   **7-7**

7-6 *and* **7-7** *400-day English clock showing week and day*

is 15 inches wide and weighs over 25 pounds. Engraved on the brass plinth is the name B. Parker, Bury St. Edmunds. This Parker was a great-great-uncle of the present owner of the clock and was by trade a gun-smith. The clock is dated *circa* 1845–50.

Fig. 7-6 shows an almost identical 400-day English fusee wound skeleton clock. There is a slight difference in the date mechanisms, cups have been introduced to support the movement, and the brass base is of rectangular shape.

In Fig. 7-7 it can be seen that the centre-wheel arbor, which was

On this are approximately seventy world-wide geographical locations, including that of Greenwich, so that the time of the day at each of these places can be indicated.

The clock, which is housed in a glass case, is unsigned. Its dimensions are $17\frac{1}{2}$ inches high by 11 inches wide and 6 inches deep. It is in the collection of S. P. Lehv of New York, U.S.A., and is dated about 1850.

A really remarkable skeleton year clock is shown in Figs. 7-11 and 7-12. The lavishness of decoration includes a lyre-shaped frame, a pair of griffins set as if guarding the whole edifice, a lion's mask, and two serpents at its summit. The quality of the castings and motifs must make this clock one of the finest year clocks designed.

All the fitments, including the bezels and subsidiary dials, are immaculately chased in fine ormolu.

The year movement is driven by two going barrels, their great wheels meshing into a single pinion. Each great wheel has been amazingly fashioned and fretted out into fourteen petal-like crossings radiating from the barrel to the outer rim. There are 196 teeth on each wheel. Fig. 7-13 gives a clear idea of their structure, as well as the rear barrel caps, with cut-out spokes to show the mainsprings therein, and the attendant ratchet and clickwork. The movement is wound from the rear.

Incorporated in the clock is a form of Debaufre escapement which involves a double escape-wheel. The ornate dial carries Arabic figures placed on enamelled discs or circles. The four subsidiary dials at the top are: at the summit, encircled by the two serpents, months of the year; at the left, days of the week; on the right, daily planetary signs of the week; and beneath, the days of the month. The dials on left and right

7-9

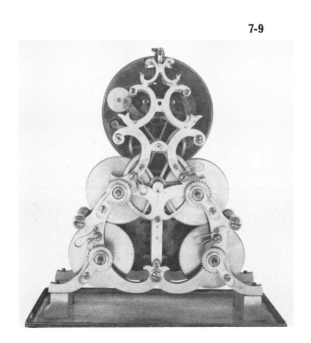

7-8

7-10

7-8 *and* **7-9** *French year clock with world time dial and calendar*

7-10 *Helical hairspring at the top*

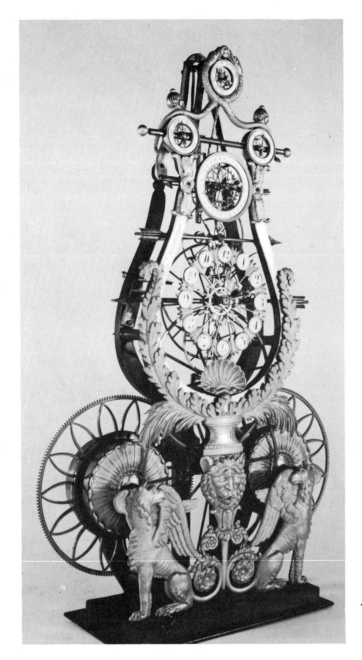

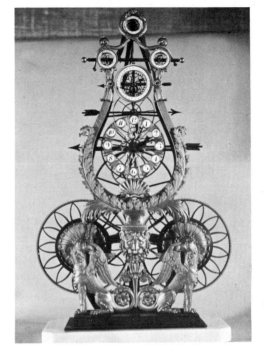

7-12

7-13

7-11 *to* **7-13** *Lyre clock with double escape-wheel that runs for a year*

have seven-pointed star wheels, in their centres, as is common on French clocks.

On the left arm of the lyre frame is engraved the name J. G. Aeits and, on the opposite arm, a Tongres. The clock stands $20\frac{1}{2}$ inches tall, $13\frac{1}{2}$ inches wide and 6 inches deep. Dated *circa* 1810, it is from the collection of Dr. S. P. Lehv of New York, U.S.A.

Musical clocks

A musical clock has a fascination of its own and is a rarity in skeleton form. That shown in Fig. 7-14 is exceptional not only for this reason but for its quite remarkable complexity.

This special musical skeleton clock has the unusual feature of incorporating four separate trains of gears – the going, striking, quarter striking, and musical. It is fusee wound, employing chains. In Fig. 7-14 the four winding arbors can just about be made out from the maze of mechanism on the front frame, including lifting pieces, snails, repeat arms, cams, intermediate wheels, rod linkages, and the like.

The going fusee arbor is practically flush with the frame. A wheel has been fitted to the fusee arbor proper which gears into an intermediate wheel upon which is fitted a winding arbor and this arbor is pivoted on the main frame and cocked. In planting the train it became obvious that the fusee arbor proper could not project from its normal place, owing to the positioning of the hour wheel. Just below 12 o'clock can be seen the platform lever escapement with its index.

The clock chimes at each quarter hour and can be made to use either the eight bells or strike on four gongs. After the full quarters have been struck, the hour is sounded upon a rich deep gong and is followed by a tune. This tune is changed automatically each day, a hymn being selected for the Sabbath. At the conclusion of the hymn, two deep gongs are struck separately to denote Amen.

7-15

7-14 *and* **7-15** *Very complex musical clock with annual calendar*

7-14

The automatic tune change indicator, with its hand, is clearly visible at the bottom left. A short steel rod with a worm gear at each end runs from it to a cam which motivates the thrust arm of the tune pin barrel between X and XI o'clock.

The following seven melodies are incorporated: the hymn Great God what do I see and hear; God Save the Queen; The Blue Bells of Scotland; The Minstrel Boy; March of the Men of Harlech; Auld Lang Syne; Home Sweet Home.

A peal of sixteen bells is used to form the music, these being struck by double hammers which are allocated to each bell.

A separate peal of eight bells, together with a four-gong arrangement, is used solely for the quarter striking sequences. As can be seen in Fig.

115

7-16

7-17

7-15 this makes a most impressive array, with the line-up of two sets of bells and the massive gong standards. (The quarter gongs have been removed to allow for photography.)

Apart from the conventional striking mechanisms, there are pull repeat actions so that the clock can be made to sound the complete cycle, or an individual choice at any time. Silent and strike controls are applied to all sections.

The engraved chapter ring has Roman numerals, the outside edge being scalloped. Above 12 o'clock a subsidiary dial indicates the days of the month. An excellent view is given of both the star wheel and the roller jumper. Note also the lengthy right-angled linkage carried to this

7-18

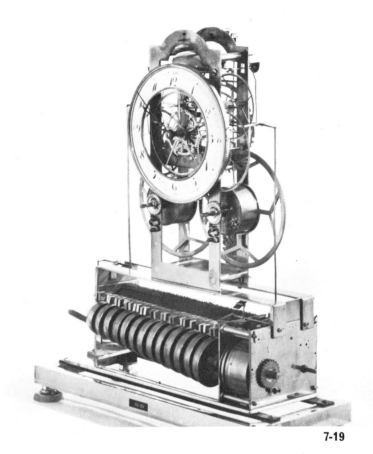

7-19

7-18 *and* **7-19** *Two more views of the musical clock in 7-17*

summit. At the base in the right-hand corner a subsidiary dial shows the day of the week.

The large, saw-toothed dial on the centre at the bottom is divided into twelve sections, each representing a month and inscribed with its name. Each tooth is calibrated with the appropriate day of the month, so there are 365 teeth.

The clock goes for eight days. For those interested in statistics, the movement is 16 inches high, 12 inches wide, and 8 inches deep. It is housed in a mahogany inlay case which stands 36 inches high, 24 inches wide, and is 12½ inches deep, and closely resembles the canopy top of a longcase clock, as shown in Fig. 7-16.

Of special interest is the brass skeleton mask which is permanently fitted to the case (as shown by comparing Figs. 7-14 and 7-16) against which the movement rests in a flush position and from which various

levers protrude, enabling one to control the musical and chiming mechanism.

There is no doubt that this clock was specially commissioned. It carries the name Frodsham, London, and is dated *circa* 1850. It is from the collection of Norman Langmaid of Washington, U.S.A.

The musical clock in Fig. 7-17 has its bells and barrel in the base. Immediately noticeable is the extremely large count-wheel or locking-plate on the back, shown in Fig. 7-18. This wheel almost spans the entire width of the rear frame, being 4½ inches in diameter, and round the edge are slots controlling the blows for both hours and quarters. The count-wheel is fitted concentrically on top of a toothed wheel which in turn meshes with a pinion carrying the pin-wheel which causes the hammer to strike the bell at the top.

Referring to the same picture, we find that the pin-wheel has lost its regular position in the striking train; moreover, it is not planted between the frames but is carried on the arbor square normally occupied by the count-wheel. The usual practice in French striking trains is for the striking great wheel, with its extended arbor, to be squared for the pur-pose of carrying the count-wheel. The steel striking hammer arbors, in

117

21, VICTORIA STREET,
HOLMFIRTH,_____192

M_____

Bᵒˢ of Coldwells, The Jewellers,

Watchmakers, Jewellers, Opticians and Clock Manufacturers.

Repairs of every description.
Clocks Wound by Yearly Contracts. | Moderate Prices.
Sound Workmanship. | Cash Buyers of Old Gold and Silver, Artificial Teeth; Second-hand Watches Diamond and other Gem Jewellery.

7-20 *Coldwell's notepaper and a cutting from the 'Daily Chronicle' (now the 'Daily Mail') Leeds edition, of October 15, 1926. The name is spelt wrongly in the newspaper*

their vertical position, are of the earliest verge form, with flat faces or pallets actuated by the pins on the pin-wheel, as opposed to the normal hammer tail.

The two brass striking hammers, which are horizontal, are friction tight on the tops of the squares of the hammer arbors. They strike on two bells at each quarter. The first quarter is sounded as a ting-tang, the second as two ting-tangs, and so on. Immediately after the fourth quarter has struck, the hours are sounded on the two bells together. When this ceases, it is followed by a melody which is played on the thirteen hemispherical bells seen below the movement. Double hammers are allocated to each bell.

The cylinder or roller plays ten tunes and automatically changes to a different tune at each hour, which is performed on the usual cam system, and can be identified at the extreme right-hand corner in Fig. 7-19. The changeover bar runs parallel to and underneath the cylinder. An early form of motive power is employed to drive the musical section, the fusee wind. The two wire-like or strip arms projecting at right-angles left and right of the movement lead to the musical mechanism. One is for the let-off and stopping of the musical melodies, whilst the other is for the melody change.

From Figs. 7-17 and 7-19, it may be seen that both trains are driven by going barrels, an interesting fact being the size of the train wheels. The great wheels have a diameter of 6 inches; the second wheel in the time train has a diameter of 4 inches, and the escape-wheel is $3\frac{1}{4}$ inches in diameter.

There are 116 teeth on the escape-wheel, the clock employing an anchor escapement. One can see in Fig. 7-19 that the pallet cock has been positioned at the left top of the frame, the cock dropping over the projecting post or pillar, and being pinned and screwed to the frame.

A rod linkage at right angles connects the pallets to the pendulum rod,

7-21 *and* **7-22** *Movement and dial of Coldwell's musical clock*

there being no crutch. In place of the original silk suspension a Brocot suspension has been incorporated, giving the normal rise and fall to adjust the pendulum, whose sunburst bob is in ormolu.

The Y formations of the crossings of the great wheels (a very French characteristic) is carried throughout both trains, but omitted from the motion work. Of particular interest in Fig. 7-19 is the stop work on the barrel caps and the fine steel clickwork attending the ratchets.

The rectangular frame carrying the trains is of rafter construction and is $12\frac{1}{2}$ inches high, $5\frac{1}{2}$ inches wide, and only 2 inches deep. On overall measurements, however, the musical clock stands $18\frac{1}{2}$ inches high, 12 inches wide, and $6\frac{1}{2}$ inches deep. The enamelled chapter ring is seven inches in diameter and has Arabic figures with a pair of steel hands. This fits into an ormolu bezel of cord design. Four knurled ormolu feet support the whole assembly.

The clock goes for eight days and is signed Sagnien, à Montreuil. It is dated *circa* 1780, and is from the Hagans Clock Manor Museum, Evergreen, Colorado, U.S.A.

A musical and chiming four-train longcase skeleton clock was the achievement of George Henry Coldwell of Holmfirth, Yorkshire, in 1906. When discussing the clock later, he casually mentioned that the work entailed was carried out in his spare time, and took some seventeen years to complete.

Coldwell was born at Kirkburton, Yorks., the son of a clock designer, and served his apprenticeship with Clarks, in Cross Church Street,

Huddersfield. He opened his first shop in Mirfield where he remained for ten years, subsequently taking possession of much larger premises in Holmfirth. Some idea of the size of these premises can be gauged from the picture which appeared in the *Daily Chronicle*, Leeds edition, on October 15, 1926 (see Fig. 7-20), where we see Mr. Coldwell standing between his two shop windows.

He was modest by nature, kindly, and studious. He was a watchmaker who became deeply interested in broader aspects of engineering and accumulated considerable knowledge of the subject through his studies. His shop, it was said, was the haven of jewellery representatives who knew that he could be easily persuaded to purchase rings, brooches, etc., by the gross instead of the dozen, which was more suitable for a small town business such as his. He had little business acumen, and whatever profits were gleaned from his efforts he spent in purchasing volume after volume of textbooks on engineering and mathematics.

From his clock drawings, he cut out the patterns in brass and steel and numbered them, with the assistance given by his two apprentices. Albert Hirst, one of these apprentices, recalls that there was a small workshop at 21 Victoria Street, Holmfirth, where he helped in the making of both the main dial and the pendulum. The movement itself was made at a much larger workshop situated at 4 Victoria Market. Here Coldwell had three various sized lathes and wheel-cutting and gear machines.

His longcase clock stands over 8 feet 6 inches high and houses a skeleton clock almost 3 feet 6 inches wide and 22 inches deep – a movement of turret clock proportions! The main dial is separate from the movement, being driven by rods and bevel gears.

Fig. 7-21 shows a side view of the movement. He used lantern pinions throughout the four trains. The wheel driving the musical barrel is a fine

example of lantern pinion work, showing the trundles or steel rods positively engaging the great wheel of the musical train, whilst robust shrouds or bosses hold these steel pieces in place. The frame is sturdy and of turret-clock design, built in tiers.

There is a vertical fly or fan, with adjustable speed vanes, to control striking, driven by a robust worm pinion. It can be seen on the left in Fig. 7-22.

The drive to the hands is from the rod with a universal joint at its end from the top of the movement. Bevel gearing is introduced to drive these rods, which eventually connect up with the main dial assembly. The tune barrel is also driven by bevel gears. The barrels, around which the lines of the driving weights are wound, are not grooved and have been left plain.

There is a four-legged gravity escapement which it is not easy to see through the maze and mass of striking and musical mechanism situated on the front frame.

Looking at the clock from the side, one can immediately recognise that under the dial there is a very highly complicated mechanism, the bevelled gearing standing out in great prominence.

Fig. 7-22 shows the front of the movement. A silvered chapter ring, engraved with Arabic figures, is set in contrast against the many intricate parts. The purpose of this separate dial (when a main dial is incorporated) is to show what time the main dial is indicating if it is out of sight, or to give Greenwich Mean Time. It is also known as a 'pilot dial'.

That this clock was a labour of love can be guessed from the hour and quarter striking mechanisms. Fanciful designs have been fashioned and scrolled into the racks, rack hooks, lifting pieces, hour snail, etc., the motion work alone having escaped. A four-toothed escape-wheel is just visible above the 6 o'clock. Whether by accident or design, the centres remain on the four winding arbors.

Clocks with complex mechanisms usually have unreadable dials, but in this case distinct Arabic brass figures have been designed to stand out in clear relief on the silvered chapter ring. The arrangement of the two subsidiary lunar and tidal dials is identical with, and taken from, the invention of James Ferguson, an eminent astronomer and mechanic who made orreries and tidal clocks in the mid-eighteenth century.

The left-hand subsidiary dial (at 9 o'clock in Fig. 7-22) gives two separate readings on two concentric circles. The outer circle is divided into two separate twelve hours, thus giving a twenty-four-hour reading, with half and quarter divisions. The inner dial readings give the age of the moon up to twenty-nine and a half days, with the inner rim showing the engraved markings 'Noon' and 'Night'.

The right-hand subsidiary dial shows the different states of the tides, together with high and low tides, and their state at any time of the day. The ellipse-type centre is engraved and represents high water at its pointed ends, and low tide at the sides. In a strip underneath, the perpetual calendar gives the day of the week, the day of the month, and the month of the year in digital form.

Beneath 12 o'clock a curved brass strip has engraved on it a degree scale, inscribed on the left with 'sun slow', and on the right 'sun fast'. A sun hand points to the scale to indicate the equation of time, i.e. the number of minutes by which time by the sundial is fast or slow of clock time. Below this hand the maker's name, George H. Coldwell, Holmfirth, can be seen. The steel hands are serpentine and, completing the dial, four gilt cupid spandrels are mounted in each corner.

The arch portion of the brass dial carries an engraved silvered strip with the old proverb 'Time and Tide Wait for no Man'. The background has a painted sky and from the circular aperture can be seen each phase of the changing moon. Between the two cliffs is a plate painted blue which rises and falls with the tides.

There are three sets of bells and chimes, eight Harrington patent tubes being used for the main set. Sixteen hammers play one of the six melodies every three hours, after the hour quarters have struck. These are played at 12, 3, 6, and 9 o'clock. There are also sixteen rod chimes and eight bells, which give many combinations for playing at each quarter.

Selections can be played on either or both rods, and bells can be played at the same time. Fig. 7-21 shows the hammers and their screwed-down hammer springs.

Westminster and Whittington chimes can be actuated for the quarter hours. The hours are struck on four gong rods. The clock has an automatic mechanism which, on Sundays only at 10.25 a.m. and at 6.25 p.m., sets off a peal of Kent treble bells to ring the parishioners to church.

The six melodies played are: Holy, Holy, Holy; Scenes that are Brightest; Lead Kindly Light; Home Sweet Home; Paradise o Paradise; and Through the Night of Doubt and Sorrow.

The going train carries a 12-pound weight, the hour striking weight is 12 pounds, the quarter chiming weight 40 pounds, and the musical weight 30 pounds. A mercurial pendulum of regular design has 7 pounds of mercury in its glass container. The clock goes for eight days.

The movement contains some 2,500 parts, and has nearly 500 screws. All the parts are numbered. The brass parts were polished with emery stick, buffed and lacquered, and all the steel parts were polished, burnished, and nickel-plated and weighed 400 pounds.

The clock was placed on exhibition in one of the windows of Coldwell's shop for the public to see, together with a full description of the mechanism and its capabilities. People came from far away to view this monumental piece of horology.

The mahogany case (Fig. 7-23) to house the clock was another example of Coldwell's craftsmanship, being practically finished when, on September 8, 1926, he died, at the early age of fifty-two.

He is buried at Napton, Mirfield, near Huddersfield. The clock eventually was sent to Canada where it still remains.

Scottish approach

An example of the Scottish approach to frame design is given in the three-train fusee wound quarter-chiming and musical skeleton clock (Fig. 7-24).

In this instance the frame is of simple scroll pattern, the casting being finely chased and gilt, as is the decorative pendulum bob. The exceptionally high quality movement has a dead-beat escapement and spoked fusee great wheels.

The exotic fretted dial frame is unusual for having Roman numerals on porcelain chapters which fit into gilt frames and are detachable.

The musical mechanism (which is of Continental manufacture) plays eight tunes, each melody running for approximately 45 seconds. It plays once every hour, the tunes moving on progressively. There are no repeats to the tunes, neither can any alteration be made manually.

The pin-barrel or cylinder is driven by a gong barrel and the melodies are played on 19 bells. There are 42 hammers attending these bells – some bells have two hammers allocated to them, others have three, to enable rapid striking in the required sequences. Some of the tunes played are: Auld Lang Syne; The Keel Row; Ilkla Moor; God Save the Queen; and Highland Laddie.

A glass aperture, front and rear in the wooden casket-shaped base enables the musical mechanism to be seen. Fig. 7-25 shows the rear view.

The clock goes for eight days. On the left-hand plinth, the name J. Crawford is engraved and, on the opposite side, Glasgow. The clock is dated *circa* 1850. Its overall height is 2 feet $7\frac{3}{4}$ inches and the base is 1 foot $9\frac{5}{8}$ inches by $12\frac{1}{2}$ inches deep. The clock is in the custody of The Royal Scottish Museum, Technological Department, Edinburgh.

Three longcase skeleton clocks

The use of internal wheels in clock trains is rare except in early turret clocks. This form of gearing was mainly used in the early eighteenth century for the sun and planet wheels in orreries. It was seldom used in

7-26

7-25

7-25 *Back of the clock in 7-24. The musical cylinder is in the base*

7-26 *Parts of a longcase skeleton clock by Dobson of Leeds. It is assembled in 7-27*

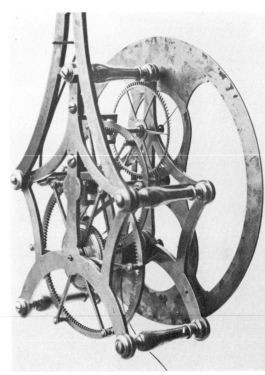

7-27

domestic clock construction. Dobson of Leeds, Yorkshire, however, made a skeleton regulator clock with internally toothed wheels.

In this clock the frame is built up of curves or arcs, and is $\frac{3}{16}$ inch thick. The design of the frame was intended to show off at their best the great wheel and seconds wheel, with their clearly-defined internal teeth. The exploded movement in Fig. 7-26 gives a complete picture of these six-spoked wheels. The ends of the crossings are of boss formation to which the spacer collets are riveted, the rim of the wheel being screwed on to the spacers. (The same principle was adopted in the early eighteenth century when inside locking plates were riveted to the striking great wheels on both fusee and longcase clocks.) The brass spacer collets are about $\frac{3}{8}$ inch high.

In Fig. 7-27 the internal toothed second wheel can be seen to engage the escape-wheel pinion.

An almost rectangular cock is employed, which to a clockmaker is somewhat similar to a lantern chuck in shape, part of one side being cut

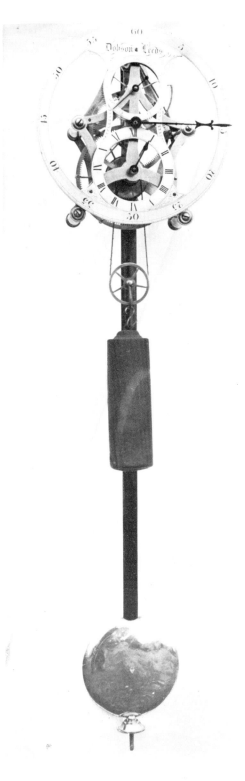

7-29

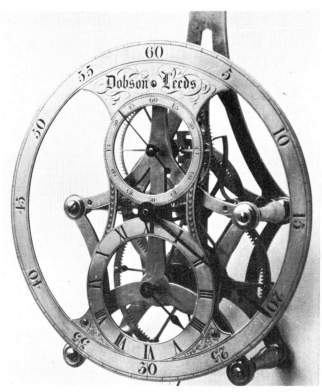

7-28

away to accommodate the second wheel. The pinion of the second wheel is screwed into a brass stud and there is therefore no arbor.

The train of the internal wheel regulator is as follows:

Main internal wheel	144 teeth, $\frac{1}{8}$ inch thick
Second internal wheel	120 teeth, $\frac{1}{16}$ inch thick
Escape-wheel	90 teeth
Second wheel pinion	12 leaves
Escape-wheel pinion	6 leaves

The pallets have a span of some 28 teeth (Fig. 7-28), the escapement being dead-beat. Note the unique positioning of the pallets, engaging the escape-wheel from the lower right-hand side. The complete movement is shown in Fig. 7-29. A heavy rectangular brass bar is fitted to the top of the back frame and is bolted to the roof of the case. To its centre tongue the movement is screwed. Both front and rear frames are colleted and screwed to the finely-turned pillars.

The pendulum rod is wood and has a brass-covered lead bob. There is no motion work, the hands being pushed, friction-tight, on to their respective arbors. The dial is simple, clear, nicely engraved, and practically devoid of decoration. It is, of course, silvered. The clock goes for eight days.

The maintaining power ratchet-wheel has engraved on its face the name J. Prince, Leeds.

Dobson of Leeds is briefly mentioned in Britten's *Old Clocks and Watches and their Makers*, and Dinsdale's book *Old Clockmakers of Yorkshire* also has a passing reference. J. Prince of Leeds is recorded as having constructed the turret clock in the Commercial Buildings, Leeds, for a fee of £80 in 1800.

The internal regulator is dated *circa* 1825, and is from the collection of Mr. F. J. Johnson of Martley Hillside, Worcester.

It is always pleasing to see different styles and shapes of clock movements and to be able to recognise them easily. Such is the facility afforded by the skeleton clock. An unusual one once seen and readily remembered is the longcase skeleton clock incorporating a gravity escapement.

An example of such a movement is shown in Fig. 7-30. The unique feature is that the rafter type of frame is of pyramidal or triangular formation. Others have found that it corresponds with the capital letter A, whilst a colleague reminded me that it is of similar shape and style

to that of a large clock displayed at the Great Exhibition and called the 'Alpha'.

The escape-wheel and pallet arms are just under 12 o'clock, the latter looking like a pair of curved calipers. The arms are suspended behind 12 o'clock. Beat adjustment can just be seen at the base of the seconds dial, seeming to touch the bosses of the hands. Some teeth of the maintaining power ratchet-wheel can just be seen at the bottom of the barrel of the great wheel on the left. The short flat steel pendulum rod has at its base two keyholes. On to these is slipped the pendulum proper, a common feature of the French Morbier or Comtoise clocks.

Striking is by rack and is conventional, the lifting piece jutting out like a wishbone. The silvered skeleton chapter ring is plain and simple and cut out into Roman numerals. It has spot indentations for the minutes with a pair of moon-style hands in steel.

The movement runs for eight days and is supported on a heavy brass bracket. A wooden rod with a cast-iron pendulum bob painted gold is used. The brass-covered lead driving weight weighs 15 pounds and the movement is housed in a regulator arched-top mahogany case with glass-fronted door and stands 5 feet 10 inches high. No name appears on this clock, which is dated *circa* 1850. It is from the collection of Mr. H. G. Best of Llangollen, Wales.

An amateur horologist and enthusiast who has made forty or more complicated clocks for his own edification and use, is included in this chapter. All his clock movements have been brilliantly executed with traditional craftsmanship, and are on a par with those of any professional.

Year clocks, complicated chiming clocks, longcase gravity clocks, even grand sonnerie carriage clocks, came from his hands. He took them all in his stride.

It was natural for him to enter the ranks of skeleton clockmakers and make a choice longcase skeleton clock. Not a single item was purchased ready made – all wheels, pinions, piercing, hands, dials, engraving, small castings, even the case itself, was the sole work of this one man, Mr. C. B. Reeve of Hastings.

This longcase skeleton clock was made with only a photograph from a trade journal of a clock by R. N. Pickering of London. Mr. Reeve produced not only a faithful copy, but introduced some revolutionary and revealing ideas (Figs. 7-31 and 7-32).

The plates have been beautifully executed and fretted from $\frac{1}{8}$ inch thick brass, the train having a great wheel of 168 teeth to a pinion of 14 to the centre wheel. The centre wheel has 112 teeth, the third wheel 105, and the escape-wheel 30 teeth, all having pinions of 14 (lantern) to a dead-beat escapement.

The great wheel is $4\frac{1}{2}$ inches in diameter. All wheels were cut with a forty-two diametrical pitch cutter. The driving barrel is $1\frac{3}{4}$ inches in diameter and is screw cut.

7-32 *Movement of the clock in 7-31*

7-33 *Adjustable pallets of the dead-beat escapement*

7-33

A Vulliamy-type dead-beat escapement is incorporated (with adjustable pallets), as shown in Fig. 7-33. Mr. Reeve is revolutionary inasmuch as his dental experience in plastics gave him the idea of making the adjustable pallets in this material. All the bearings, which have the appearance of jewels, are made in plastics material. These, in turn, are sunk in brass cups with the flange of each fixed to the movement by three screws. After many years of use, there are no signs whatever of wear.

He has hinged the pallet arms to a differential screw to give minute adjustment for correct depthing. (Incidentally, Vulliamy adjustable pallets found considerable favour on the Continent and are common in Vienna regulators, but of course without the differential screw to the pallet arms.)

The set-in-beat adjustment is at the rear of the pallet arbor. An eccentric ring has been fitted (as in most French clocks) to enable adjustment to raise or lower the pallets.

The clock is of eight-day duration and has a seconds gridiron pendulum. The driving weight is $5\frac{1}{2}$ pounds with double gut line on a fretted pulley. The movement is housed in a walnut case. The whole clock took some nine months to complete and is *c.* 1929.

7-31 *Longcase skeleton clock by C. B. Reeve of Hastings*

8-1 *Austrian skeleton clock with constant force escapement (remontoire) that runs for three months*

CHAPTER 8

AUSTRIAN, AMERICAN, AND NOVELTY CLOCKS

Austrian skeletons

Viennese skeleton clocks have a character all of their own and I can do no better in introducing an example of these masterpieces than to give a quotation from Mr. Charles Allix: 'the Parisian skeleton clocks of the year close to 1800 show an elegance of conception and a mechanical refinement unequalled save by a few clocks made in Vienna'.

He refers to the delicately-made three-month skeleton clock shown in Fig. 8-1. In this clock everything makes for perfection and grace. It is a veritable masterpiece of delicate formation. The front frame is of symmetrical design, robust and unusually thick, measuring exactly half an inch.

The dexterity of the Viennese horologists can be best exemplified by considering, for a moment, that the whole train of wheels employed in the working of the movement (excepting the pin-wheel), are all just over one millimetre in thickness and look alarmingly frail. The diameter of the great wheel is five and a half inches, and all the pinion work has high numbers. The small steel winding ratchet-wheel with its clickwork mechanism is planted inside, behind the brass strip which constitutes the rear frame, and is practically hidden from view.

The division of one train into two is achieved by remontoire. The striking train has a great wheel and concentric count wheel. Both the striking great wheel and the count wheel (or locking plate), turn every twelve hours and are kept wound by an arbor that rotates in eleven hours. These two wheels have a diameter of $2\frac{3}{4}$ inches. The clock is a quarter striking ting-tang on two silvered bells. Worthy of mention are the long blue steel limbs, or rods, employed as lifting pieces and hammer tails to actuate the striking sequences.

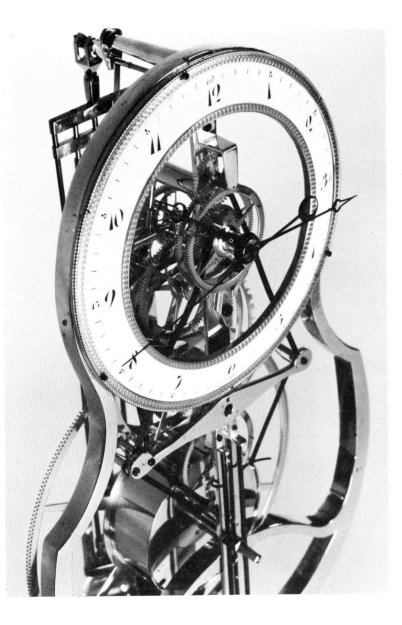

quarter inches in length. At their top (lower part of Fig. 8-2) can be seen their curved tails engaging the tails of lifting pieces. The hammer arbors are separately cocked, both top and bottom, the bottom hammer cocks carrying the set springs to the hammer arbors. The two brass striking hammers can be seen at the base of the movement, one positioned to the left and the other to the right.

A pin-wheel dead-beat escapement is incorporated, having two pallets on a single arm in step formation. An inverted knife-edge steel suspension has been included, upon which hangs the pendulum and which is suspended by a steel swivelled stirrup link (top of Fig. 8-2).

The half-seconds pendulum has five rods for compensation and carries a fine lenticular bob. The centre seconds hand turns twice in every minute, thus giving half seconds.

The enamelled chapter ring, with its Arabic figures, is a design peculiar to Viennese clocks. It is encased in a finely-decorated ormolu bezel and finished off with a pair of steel Empire design hands. The movement stands 11 inches high and rests on an 8-inch oval Cipollino green flecked marble base, supported by four matching ormolu feet. The clock is dated *circa* 1800, is unsigned, and goes for three months. It is from the collection of Major Anthony Heathcote.

An interesting Austrian skeleton clock which presents many unique features is the larger one in Fig. 8-3. This clock, of rafter construction, has a going barrel and can be wound by two independent winding arbors. There is an arbor proper to the going barrel, whilst the intermediate, or idle wheel, has a fixed arbor, which in turn is placed between the main frames. This intermediate wheel gears into the main ratchet-wheel and is clearly visible outside the main assembly with its winding square below 6 o'clock.

A side view of it appears in Fig. 8-4. The practice of introducing an intermediate wheel or wheels to the winding mechanism stems back to the early days of horology. In this case the purpose is to avoid the centre seconds hand, which would inevitably foul if the main arbor were used.

The brass double tongue piece in the centre of the arch below this wheel, is the balance cock, retaining the top balance pivot. It may be seen clearly in Fig. 8-4. The chain draped below, on which the pulley rides is, in fact, the counterweight to the weight-driven train remontoire which is employed. The remontoire weight arrangement with its endless chain and attendant pulleys is shown in Fig. 8-5.

The clock incorporates a pin-wheel escapement which can also be seen in the same illustration in the centre of the back plate. The pallet arms engaging the pins comprise the caliper-like piece on the left of the weight. A bar at the base of the frame carries the horizontal balance-wheel,

In Fig. 8-2 looking at the cross bar under the chapter ring, the left-hand limb, or rod, reaches to the face of the cannon pinion (on which the minute hand is fitted) which carries four quarter lifting pins. The right-hand limb leads up to the minute wheel which carries the hour striking pin. It terminates just under the minute wheel cock. The striking pin wheel is placed just under the cross bar and carries only two pins on its wheel rim.

The vertical hammer arbors are delicately fashioned, being six and a

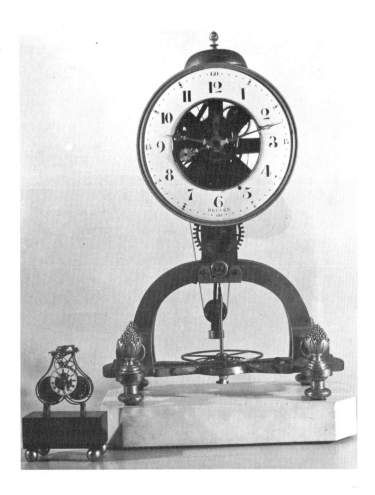

which is about four inches in diameter, together with the balance-spring pinned to its stud on the left-hand corner. The balance arbor has a crank-like formation (Fig. 8-4) to which is fitted a vertical impulse pin. As the balance oscillates to and fro, the impulse pin engages with a right angular arm (which is screwed to the pallet arbor proper), and receives impulses from the pallets.

The locking plate, or count wheel, for the striking sequences lies under the remontoire ratchet-wheel, the clock striking the hours and half hours.

The clock has centre seconds hand and a very fine pair of gilt hands which give added character to the very simple semi-circular frame which rises to a short perpendicular post. The enamelled chapter ring has bold clear Arabic figures and the inscribed signature of Druyer.

At the base of the frame and flanked at each corner to give ornamentation, are four gilt finials depicting inverted grapes in a cup fashioned in vine leaves resting on gilt feet, the whole being placed on a white marble base. The clock is 17 inches high, 12 inches wide, and 5 inches deep and is dated *circa* 1820. The miniature skeleton clock by its side, in Fig. 8-3, demonstrates by comparison the variation of size of skeleton clocks. Both are from the collection of Dr. S. P. Lehv of New York, U.S.A.

The Austrian pillar skeleton clock shown in Fig. 8-6 is a typical product

8-3 *An Austrian remontoire clock with balance wheel in the base. Beside it is a miniature American clock. See 8-15*

8-4 *and* **8-5** *Side and rear view of the Austrian clock in 8-3*

8-4

8-5

of Vienna. This particular specimen has a three train, quarter-striking spring-driven movement with a detached musical mechanism concealed in its base. In Fig. 8-7, the rear frame can be seen to be fretted out in a lyre design.

Unfortunately, the design is partially hidden by the T-shaped gong standard. The style of this gong standard and its placing in this position is a common feature of most Austrian striking clocks, skeleton or otherwise. The two hammer heads have been cut out to look like rings.

At the base, the door has been removed, disclosing the musical section. This is wound independently by pulling the cord with the bead at its end,

the action being the same as in a pull-repeat mechanism. The melodies are let off at the hour from the minute wheel in the movement above.

The skeleton dial is a little unusual, with fretted shields carrying Roman numerals, whilst the festooned inner rim has engraved on it the days of the month. The ormolu bezel is in the traditional Austrian manner, in its cord and engine-turned pattern, as also are the motifs surrounding the base, and the pronounced pillars which support the movement. The platform on the pillars is held down by the two urn finials.

The pendulum is hung by silk suspension, the bob again showing the lyre theme, which appears in the standard seen in the rear, adding support to the movement. All are of exceptionally high quality and in fine

8-8 *Weight-driven Austrian clock with perpetual calendar*

ormolu. The clock stands 19 inches high, 12 inches wide, and 7 inches deep.

Festooned under the calendar ring appears the name Anton, Hierman in Wien. The clock is dated *circa* 1810 and is from the collection of Dr. S. P. Lehv of New York, U.S.A.

Another form of Austrian pillar skeleton clock is shown in Fig. 8-8. It is a weight-driven mantel timepiece with a particularly sober outline.

In spite of the clock's simplicity, it is worth commenting on the bases and capitals into which the pillars fit and enthusing on the superb workmanship of the oval base, the whole assembly, including the bezel, being silvered.

The six-inch dial has Roman numerals. The two lower dials give, on the left, the month of the year, and, on the right, the days of the month. Although a seconds dial can be seen, the clock also has a centre seconds. It has a dead-beat escapement, together with maintaining power. The driving weight is engine-turned. The clock stands 21 inches high, is 11

8-9 *to* **8-11** *Austrian clock with three-legged gravity escapement*

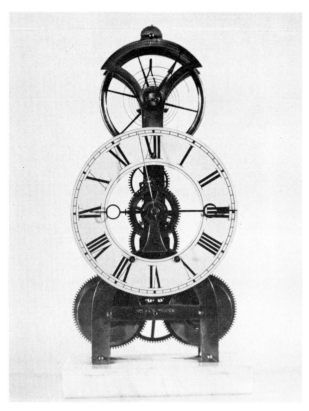

8-12 *Silas Terry experimental skeleton made in the U.S.A.*

8-13 *American skeleton clock with helix gearing*

inches wide, and 6 inches deep. It is unsigned, goes for eight days and is dated *circa* 1830. It is from the collection of Mr. Norman Langmaid of Washington D.C., U.S.A.

Fig. 8-9 shows an Austrian skeleton clock with a three-legged gravity escapement and double knife-edge suspension for the pendulum. The striking train is wound by a weight-driven remontoire employed for this purpose. The clock has quarter striking and grand sonnerie. The striking, as can be seen in Figs. 8-10 and 8-11, is on gongs, which encircle the barrel, as does the pendulum rod! The frame is of rafter construction.

The small intermediate wheel (lower left in Fig. 8-10) isolated from the movement proper and pivoted to the right-hand frame, is the winding wheel. It engages the great wheel of the tandem barrel, through which the mainspring can be seen. The clock goes for three months and is dated *circa* 1850. It is from the collection of W. Pinder of Peterborough.

Three American clocks

The American skeleton clock production did not seriously compete with other countries. The few American skeleton clocks that still exist were, in the main, experimental and do not emulate the work of such countries as France, England and Austria.

Of immense interest, however, is the Silas Terry experimental skeleton timepiece seen in Fig. 8-12. A simple frame is introduced, the train being planted in an almost vertical line. Towering above the dial is the huge balance-wheel and hairspring with its large index and pointer. The movement has a centre seconds hand and is driven by a pair of going barrels. The clock is stamped on the cross-bar with the name Silas B. Terry.

In Fig. 8-13 is an American skeleton clock with helical gearing. The frame has some English characteristics and also a French flavour in that it incorporates silk suspension, with a plain form of rise and fall adjustment for the pendulum. The escape-wheel has 120 teeth, the escapement being an anchor (or recoil). Fig. 8-14 gives a clear indication of the helical gearing, both on the wheels and pinions. Note also the turned pillar work. The clock stands 11 inches high, 5 inches wide and $3\frac{1}{4}$ inches deep.

What must be described as a minor gem is the miniature skeleton clock 3 inches high, $2\frac{1}{2}$ inches wide, and $\frac{1}{2}$ inch deep shown in Fig. 8-15. An idea of its size is given in an earlier picture (Fig. 8-3).

8-14

8-15

The heart-shaped frame holds a lever platform escapement with a solid horizontal balance. Being an experimental clock it can be readily seen that, at one time, some provision had been made for the unoccupied hole in the frame just above the contrate wheel, possibly for a previous scheme. The movement is fusee wound. The chain can just be discerned running on to the barrel, through which the mainspring can be seen. A pair of sun hands is fitted on to the typically American squared centre arbor. The clock is unsigned and is dated *circa* 1850.

These three American skeleton clocks are from the collection of Dr. S. P. Lehv of New York, U.S.A.

Novelty clocks

The movement of an unusual Austrian skeleton clock is shown in Fig. 8-16. It is in the collection of Mr. Norman Langmaid of Washington D.C., U.S.A., and is a one-wheel clock. The wheel has 150 teeth and revolves once every five minutes. There is an anchor escapement that spans fifty of these teeth. The clock has a seconds pendulum and fixed seconds hand. The mercurial pendulum bob has three glass tubes to hold the mercury in the bob, and weighs 15 pounds. The driving weight of the clock is only 9 ounces.

8-16 *Austrian one-wheel skeleton movement, which goes in a longcase*

8-17

8-18

Fig. 8-18 shows an American experimental skeleton clock with a floating chronometer escapement. The balance has been stylised in the form of a ship's steering wheel. It is also from the collection of Dr. S. P. Lehv.

Throughout the ages, novelty clocks have appeared in one form or another. It was therefore not surprising that some occur among skeleton clocks.

The miniature skeleton clock, 10 inches high, shown in Figs. 8-19 and 8-20 is made entirely of ivory, as is the carved pendulum. The movement is supported on columns or pillars and is fusee wound. Unfortunately the gut line has been severed. The clock is signed Edward Bates, Kingsland, 1858 (Fig. 8-19). It is still one more from the collection of Dr. S. P. Lehv.

Of exceptional interest were skeleton clocks made of papier mâché.

8-19

8-17 and **8-18** *Experimental American ship's wheel clock with chronometer escapement*

8-19 *Miniature ivory clock with carved ivory pendulum*

8-20 *Back of the ivory clock*

8-21 *Skeleton clock made of papier mâché. It is driven by a coil spring*

The British Horological Institute has a papier mâché skeleton clock in its museum at 35 Northampton Square, London, E.C.1. It is pendulum controlled as shown in Figs. 8-21 and 8-22, with the escape-wheel positioned above the dial. All wheels are papier mâché, which is pulped paper and glue that has been allowed to set.

For interest another papier mâché clock, belonging to Lt. Col. Lynn B. Moore, Fairfax, Virginia, U.S.A. has been included although it is not strictly a skeleton clock. It is shown in Fig. 8-22 and has a rafter frame which is made up of a combination of wood and paper. There are similarities in the two clocks.

All wheels are of papier mâché and have lantern pinions. In lieu of steel or metal, the trundles or rods are bamboo pieces that fit into both ends of the shrouds, which are of paper.

The great wheel has 120 teeth and is fitted to a rolled paper arbor approximately a quarter inch thick. The pivots of the train fit individually into pieces of cow-horn inserted into the frame, such as the upright ones seen in Fig. 8-23, carrying the escape-wheel.

It can also be seen that the pallets, again of cow-horn, are inverted to

and 'retard' printed on it. The bobs themselves have various gilt embossed paper designs which can be stuck on to suit the different models which were manufactured.

One of these models has floral motifs and the other a sunray. On both dials is printed the name N. S. Villemsen et. cie. Galerie Vivienne No. 38, together with Novelles Pendules en Carton Perfectionees. They are dated *circa* 1870.

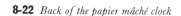

8-22 *Back of the papier mâché clock*

8-23 *and* **8-24** *Another papier mâché clock*

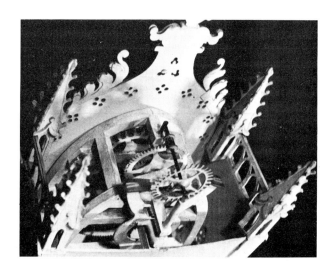

the escape-wheel, which has thirty-two teeth, and is a form of anchor escapement. (Fig. 8-22.) Pivot suspension is used. In this instance, the two fixed cow-horn conical pivots are inverted, whilst the cups are fitted to a round bar through the acute angle formed by the pallet arms.

The driving mechanism is a steel spiral spring some $4\frac{1}{2}$ inches in length and $\frac{1}{2}$-inch in diameter. The cord at the top of the spiral spring winds round the great wheel arbor, extending through this spring and the base to a winding drum, as seen in Fig. 8-24.

As the movement is being wound, the spiral spring is extended from its $4\frac{1}{2}$ inches in length to a maximum of $8\frac{3}{4}$ inches, giving enough power to motivate the clock for thirty hours.

A ratchet arrangement on the reverse side of the great wheel is to prevent unwinding, the ratchet being papier mâché and click cow-horn. There are only two wheels for the motion work. The minute hand is placed directly to the second wheel. The pendulum bob slides up and down on a wide paper band to which is pasted a chart having 'advance'

CHAPTER 9

SKELETON CLOCKS IN BUCKINGHAM PALACE

The ravages of time have taken a vast toll of important horological pieces and, sad to relate, royal clocks in royal palaces are no exception to the rule. These clocks have, in fact, suffered damage by alteration, which has changed some beyond recognition. Even the great B. L. Vulliamy is reputed to have altered and placed entirely new movements in many of the royal clocks in Buckingham Palace.

In Baillie's *Watchmakers and Clockmakers of the World*, page 65, the name of William Congreve appears and, among his various inventions the following is mentioned: 'Designed skeleton clock made by Moxon, Buckingham Palace'.

In spite of the entry being in the singular, there are *two* skeleton clocks in Buckingham Palace. Both were designed by Sir William Congreve and both were made by John Moxon. They were first acquired for Carlton House and placed in the library there, but were eventually rehoused in Buckingham Palace, where they have remained ever since.

The better known skeleton clock originally carried the 'extreme detached escapement'. This is indicated by an inscription on the top frame of the movement, which rests on a pedestal (Fig. 9-1). The other clock is housed in a long case (Fig. 9-6).

It is interesting to note that Congreve attributed considerable importance to the extreme detached escapement. It was so important to him, in fact, that he patented his version. A record of this can be found in the Patent Lists dated August 24, 1808, Patent number 3164, which reads as follows:

'That he accomplishes the same effect by a simple pendulum. A

light spring wheel of thirty teeth is unconnected with anything but the seconds hand, and a pair of pallets. Another pallet, on the same stock, is connected with a large wheel of sixty teeth. On the face of this wheel are sixty pins, and a lever acting on these locks the wheel.

'On the face of the little wheel is one pin. A seconds pendulum being set in motion, the pallets drive the little wheel, and, at the sixtieth second, the pin discharges the lever from the pins of the large wheel. This, being thus unlocked, starts forward from the action of the first mover, and one of its teeth striking the pallet of the large wheel, gives renewed motion to the pendulum. When the pin on the little wheel has passed the lever, the lever relocks the large wheel for another fifty-nine seconds.'

Fig. 9-2 is a drawing of this escapement. (Printed, 11d. See Repertory of Arts, vol. 14 (second series), p.l.; and Rolls chapel reports, 7th report,

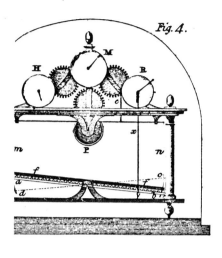

Fig. 4.

Fig. 5.

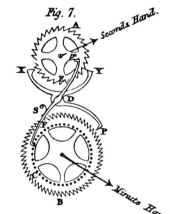

Fig. 7.

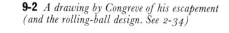

9-2

9-2 *A drawing by Congreve of his escapement (and the rolling-ball design. See 2-34)*

9-3 *Sketch from the pictorial inventory dated from 1825, showing the original double chapter ring*

9-3

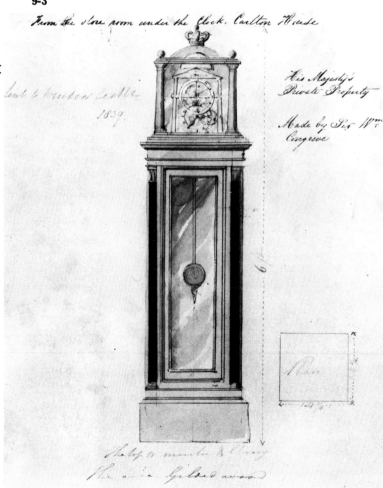

page 107.) See also Repertory of Arts Manufacturers, and Agriculture No. 79, December 1808, vol. 14 (second series), which gives a complete specification of the Congreve Patent.

That this clock was tiresome and temperamental, is apparent to records. One is an entry in the day book of one Benjamin Jutson, who was inventory clerk to George IV. The entry is dated August 24, 1808 and reads as follows:

'Delivered to Mr. Congreve, the curious clock for the measurement of time, with a pedestal from the library at Carlton House, to be regulated.'

The other is taken from the Buckingham Palace outfit bills of December 30, 1837.

'Work done by order of the Lord Chamberlain's Office by Benjamin Louis Vulliamy, 68, Pall Mall.
'Repaired and made to perform properly, a spring clock made by Moxon, with extreme detached escapement upon Sir William Congreve's principle, that goes mounted in a large skeleton frame, a

138

most complicated and troublesome machine, and new silvered, the work that had been silvered before, and lacquered the skeleton plates and all the large parts, and lacquering spirit level £4.'

This clock continued to be a source of considerable concern because of its poor timekeeping, which, in the end, caused the authorities to take some drastic action, resulting in the removal of the escapement section in which Congreve had so much faith. Fig. 9-2 shows Congreve's drawing of the escapement.

In its place was installed an Earnshaw chronometer escapement which was constructed by Charles Frodsham & Co. An inscription to this effect is engraved on the base of the platform. Unfortunately from an historical and horological viewpoint this alteration caused the removal, for all time, of the original double-silvered chapter rings which gave an unhindered view of the clock's mechanism.

The clock goes for eight days and rests on a pedestal, the whole assembly being covered by a glass shade. The original pedestal was painted to imitate lapis lazuli. Unfortunately this is now missing.

The movement itself stands 15 inches high, and is 11¾ inches wide. The clock is dated *circa* 1800.

Information and records on the second Congreve skeleton clock, housed in a longcase and seen in Fig. 9-6 are extremely scanty. The round dial has a similarity to the other clock, which immediately suggests that this clock too, had undergone a process of considerable alteration.

The inscription, which is engraved in a circle above 6 o'clock and looks like a subsidiary dial, confirms this. It says: 'Reconstructed by Chas. Frodsham & Co. Anno Domini MDCCCLXXIX'.

This is proved from a drawing of the second skeleton clock by Congreve, which forms part of a pictorial inventory made for George IV, dating from about 1825. It clearly illustrates the double chapter rings which Congreve originally conceived, to give a full view of the working mechanism. The chapter rings have been supplanted by a very plain and ordinary silvered and engraved round dial (Fig. 9-3).

When this dial is removed, the skeleton movement can be examined in some detail (as shown in Fig. 9-4). The brass rafter frames, are rectangular – the top having a pediment formation. The whole design can best be described as looking like a cage.

There are four frames in all, spaced by finely-turned brass pillars or posts. It can be readily seen that both the going and striking trains have been planted vertically. An uncommon feature is that the two fusees are positioned at the summit, and that the going side is wound from the front, whilst the striking is wound from the rear. The maintaining ratchet-wheel is readily visible, together with the considerable number of pinions employed. Note the undercutting of the pinion engaging the going fusee great wheel and the escapement with its steel helical hair-spring.

It will be noticed that the striking train is completely run down (the full chain being round the barrel). I am told that the striking section has been purposely placed out of action, and can be reinstated, if necessary, in a couple of minutes.

With the dial now removed one is faced by a number of plugged holes, seen on the two cross bars of the front frame in Fig. 9-5. It is clear, therefore, that these plugged holes carried the original chapter rings and the extreme detached escapement.

The balance can be seen to be sunk below the platform. Regulation is achieved by the removal of a small drawer – also below the platform – which can be brought forward by the knurled knob in the centre. This gives access to the rating nuts.

As in the skeleton clock previously described, Congreve utilised the identical design for his framework, incorporating, once more, four frames for this purpose, and following the same trend by positioning the going trains vertically in the front, with the striking train immediately behind.

It is difficult to ascertain what form of escapement was provided before the major re-construction undertaken by Frodsham in 1879. Regrettably no records survive, and no information is available, either from the Palace authorities or from Frodshams themselves, who still maintain the clocks at Buckingham Palace.

This clock, as it now stands, really takes the form of a striking regulator, having jewelled pallets and a dead-beat escapement. Under the dial is inscribed 'invented by William Congreve, Esq., J. Moxon fecit'.

The case is in gilt wood with inset panels, and a mirror is placed between the pendulum and weight, which falls into a compartment. The clock goes for eight days and is dated *circa* 1800. The dimensions are shown in the original drawing.

The photographs in this chapter are reproduced by gracious permission of Her Majesty the Queen.

10-1 *William Strutt, F.R.S., from a painting hanging in Kingston Hall, Nottinghamshire, the home of the Rt. Hon. Lord Belper, one of his descendants, who kindly allowed the painting to be photographed by the Paul Mellon Centre for Studies in British Art (London) Ltd. See page 99*

CHAPTER 10

MORE SKELETON CLOCKS FROM PAST AND PRESENT

After the first publication of *Skeleton Clocks* in 1969, many more pictures were received from readers by the late Bernard Royer-Collard and by the publishers. Some were identical or very similar to illustrations already appearing and others provided more revealing views of such clocks. There were also clocks with different designs of frame and movement. Some were old and some – among them the most complicated – had been made in recent years by enthusiastic craftsmen who lacked nothing of the skills of their predecessors.

A representative selection of these pictures is included as well as one of the maker William Strutt, whose likeness was not known to exist when the original publication appeared. They are in no particular order except that in general they end with the newer more complicated versions.

The tradition of the skeleton clock is different from that of most antique clocks in that a clock made with the same painstaking and thoughtful skill, especially if original in conception, will often stand with older clocks and is not despised because of its modern origins. Even copies are highly prized, if well made. Since the first edition, many makers of reproduction English skeleton clocks have gone into business, one even in Spain. Also many old plated frame clocks which have been divorced from their cases have been skeletonised to give them a new lease of life; although their origins, from the placing of the train and pillars, are often obvious to someone familiar with clocks.

The publishers are indebted for the pictures in this chapter to the Rt. Hon. Lord Belper (1); R. H. L. Sexton, U.S.A. (2); Aubrey Brocklehurst, London (3, 25); Keith Banham Ltd., London (4, 5, 11, 12, 13); Bobinet Ltd., London (6, 7); Ronald A. Lee, London (8); J. M. Wild, Sheffield (9, 14); Robert N. Schneblin, U.S.A. (10); Dr. C. R. Lattimore, U.S.A. (15, 16); E. R. Conover, Jr., U.S.A. (17, 18); N. Langmaid, U.S.A. (19); Hills of Sudbury, Suffolk (20, 21); J. A. Johnsson, Sweden (23, 24); John Stevens (24); and Maynard E. Bell, U.S.A. (26, 27).

10-2 *Bird's eye view of the variable quarter chime and hour strike flys of a cathedral clock. The turret terminals give a clear indication of the makers, John Smith and Sons of Clerkenwell. Note that the pin barrel for the chime is driven by bevel gears*

10-3 *Another model from the steam factory of John Smith and Sons in St. John's Square, Clerkenwell. It is a timepiece with decorative pendulum bob. Two lions flank the clock and in front of the pendulum bob is a 'ship's compass'*

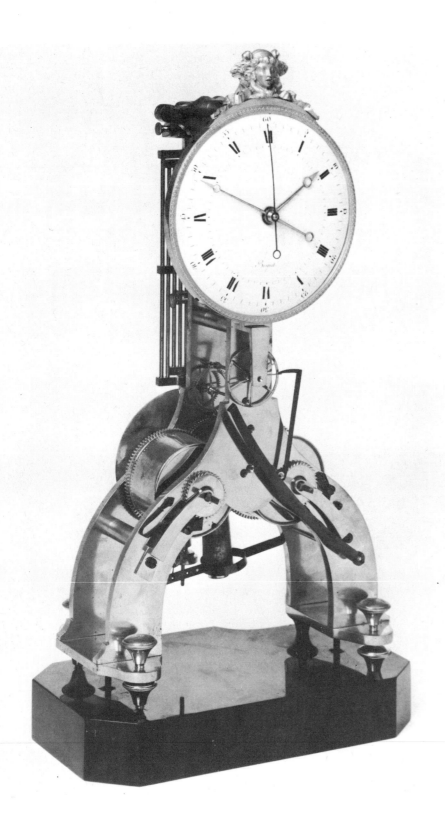

10-5 *Back of the clock in 10-4, with the pendulum removed. The spring barrels drive a weight remontoire that is wound every two minutes. The lower pulley wheel raises the weight through a Huygens endless cord drive. The upper one powers the dead beat escapement. The remontoire can be seen under the dial in 10-4*

10-6 (*Left*) *A steeple-framed timepiece with screwed-on wheels. The going barrel drives a vertically-mounted compensation balance with English lever escapement. The dial is signed Thomas Black of Kirkcaldy and an inscription on the base records this fact as well as the name of the man who moulded and cast the brass work, William D. Nelson of the same town*

10-7 (*Right*) *A clock striking one blow at the hour by an outrigged lever system. It is signed James Black of Kirkcaldy. The large spring barrel is within four reeded pillars on which the clock is mounted. The train has screwed-on wheels and there is a spring detent escapement with Earnshaw type free-sprung balance with helical spring*

10-8 *A clock by Robert Roskell of Liverpool with a Savage escapement. The wheels have six crossings (spokes) each and mesh directly instead of having pinions. The escape wheel is positioned horizontally. The $3\frac{1}{2}$-inch balance wheel has three arms carrying rating nuts, and a helical spring. The small wheel at the top of the balance arbor carries two impulse pins engaging the fork of the pallets. The two carved wires with steel balls on the ends (looking like swizzle sticks) act as a governor to prevent over-banking. The three enamelled dials indicate hours, minutes and seconds. The top finial may be a replacement for a ball and spire like the others. The frame engraving gives Roskell's address as Rio de Janeiro also*

10-9 *Plain skeleton timepiece of lyre design by Dent of 33 and 34 Cockspur Street, Charing Cross, London, with fusee drive, dead beat escapement, and spade hour hand*

10-10 *The frame of this clock, made about 1912, is in the form of the monogram AVC and ten of the chapters are lettered A.V. CHANDLER BT. The clock chimes on five true bells*

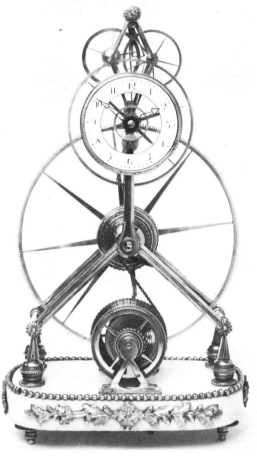

10-11

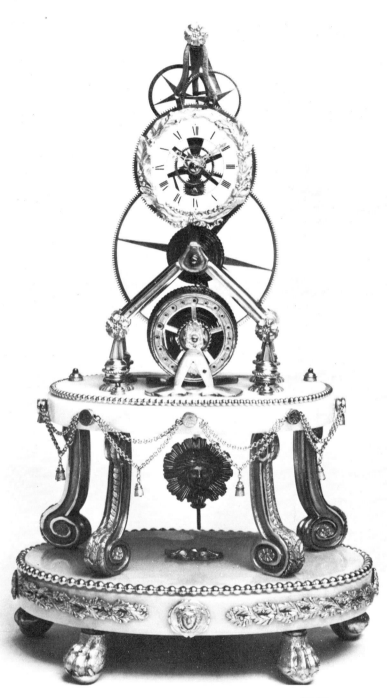

10-11, 10-12, *and* **10-13** *Three fine 18th century French skeleton clocks, all made on a similar plan with gilt frames, fusee drive, and pin-wheel escapements with pendulum. Note the large centre wheel of the clock above, which is almost identical to the 14-day clock shown in 5-10*

10-13

10-12

10-15 and **10-16** The compensated Harrison style gridiron pendulum is almost as big as the clock in this robust model with an anchor escapement, shown below

10-15

10-16

10-14 A four-hundred day or anniversary skeleton clock with an earlier type of torsion pendulum in the centre of the feet, which oscillates slowly on a thin suspension spring

10-17

10-18

10-17 *and* **10-18** *A large tourbillion (revolving) escapement is the feature of this clock with centre seconds hand. On the bottom is a plate stating, 'Reproduction of tourbillion, invented 1795, patented 1801, by Abraham Louis Breguet'. The escapement, directly behind the dial, can be seen in the illustration right*

10-19 *A skeleton clock from Austria with two wheels only. It is weight-driven and has a dead beat escapement with mercury compensated pendulum. The columns and base are blood red in colour*

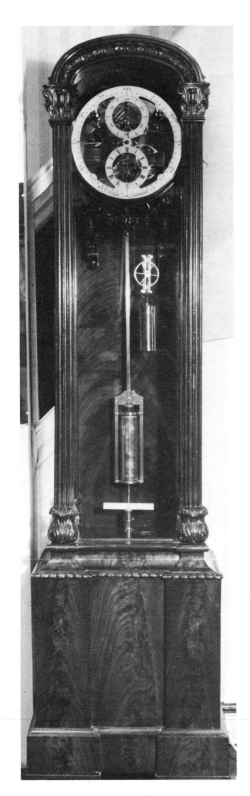

10-20

10-20 and **10-21** *A fine regulator in a mahogany case. The skeletonised movement follows the same layout as an unskeletonised one, with dead-beat escapement, jewelled pallets and mercury pendulum. Note the elegant weight pulley on the right, above*

10-22 *Timepiece with a tassel or swag style frame and fusee movement controlled by pendulum and anchor escapement*

10-23 *A similar type of clock to that above but with different 'tassels'. Both clocks are in Austria*

10-24 *The unusual feature of this fusee timepiece, completed by John Stevens in 1970 and an award winner the following year at the Model Engineering Exhibition in London, is the stainless steel frame. Note the helical hairspring, and escapement driven by a contrate wheel*

10-25 *A fine annual calendar clock showing day, date and month, made in 1970 by Malcolm Blandford, C.M.B.H.I., in the workshop of Aubrey Brocklehurst of London, S.W.7. (who took over the premises of the author of this book when he retired). The clock chimes on seven bells and strikes on a large spiral gong, the pillar and block of which can be seen on the right behind the pin barrel*

10-26 *An unique skeleton clock made in 1960 by Maynard E. Bell of Toledo, Ohio, U.S.A. It is powered by balls delivered to a 60-pocket main wheel from a 12 feet long track along which the balls roll. The track is not part of the timekeeping element as in a Congreve clock; that is the conical pendulum in the front. A movement in the base, controlled by a detent, supplies the 102 5/16 inch steel balls to the track and main wheel (seen framing the dial) so that there are 24 in the main wheel and 78 in the base and in transit at any one time*

10-27 *Another clock made, like the previous one, by Maynard E. Bell. It runs for eight days, being driven by two compounded weights with a fall of 8½ inch and has maintaining power. There is a 'rack and pinion' escapement and a floating balance suspended from a helical spring, that gives a seconds beat. The perpetual calendar shows day, date, month and moon phase. The orrery on top demonstrates the sun, earth, moon, venus and mercury in their orbits and is operated automatically by the clock or manually with a key*

CHAPTER 11

SKELETON CLOCKS AT THE GREAT EXHIBITION

Of all the controversy surrounding the skeleton clock, perhaps the most nonsensical old wives' tale is that only four clocks were ever made, and these exclusively for the Great Exhibition of 1851, held in Hyde Park.

The following paragraphs will show that this is not the case, and on the contrary, the Victorian period marked the heyday of the skeleton clock.

To confirm this issue beyond all doubt, I enlisted the help of county librarians who obtained the official catalogues. The official 'illustrated catalogue' turned out to be in three volumes, each weighed just over four pounds. They could be purchased in sets of three at the time of the exhibition, for thirty shillings. There was also an official handbook catalogue of some 350 pages, costing one shilling and threepence, which was not illustrated.

The title-page sounds awe-inspiring:

'By Authority of the Royal Commission The Official Catalogue of The Great Exhibition of the Works of Industry of all Nations – 1851'.

Volume 1 provided the necessary horological information – also under a grand title: 'Section Two – Class Ten – Philosophical, Musical, Horological and Surgical Instruments'.

In all, 131 watch and clockmakers were shown to have exhibited their products and mechanisms, some very highly specialised. From the total number of horological exhibitors only eighteen were found to have included skeleton clocks in their displays. The following is a complete list of names of these exhibitors – both from the official handbook catalogue and the illustrated descriptive catalogue – who were in any way connected with the manufacture of skeleton clocks.

As the official 'Descriptive and Illustrated Catalogue' is the more comprehensive in its contents I take my quotations from this: if the exhibitor is mentioned only in the small handbook, reference is made accordingly. The number preceding the paragraph denotes the stand number.

(27) GOWLAND, JAMES – 52 London Wall (Inventor and Manufacturer).
Skeleton clock with improved compensation pendulum, other items including Patent Tourbillon remontoire chronometer impulse imparted to the balance through the balance-spring, its stud being advanced one degree on tooth of locking plate at each oscillation.

(33) MOORE & SONS – 38 Clerkenwell Close (Manufacturer).
Chiming skeleton to go a month; skeleton clock.

(37) ROBINSON, P. – Bishop Auckland (Designer and Manufacturer).
Skeleton spring clock which strikes the hours and quarters on modulated bells; with a compensator for counteracting temperature. The clock and framework are a representation of the clock tower and entrance of the Bishop of Durham's Palace at Bishop Auckland.

(42) LAMB, J – Bicester, Oxfordshire.
Skeleton clock to go 400 days.

(43) THORNELOE, C. – Lichfield (Designer and Manufacturer).
Clock which strikes quarters and goes thirty-two days. Design Lichfield Cathedral, Gothic skeleton clock.

(47) HARVEY, —, – Stirling, Scotland (Inventor and Manufacturer).
Improvement in horology dispensing with striking work; only one wheel is used, which is placed under the hour-wheel and receives motion from it. This improvement can be supplied to almost any other timepieces, especially to skeleton timepieces; the article exhibited is the original invention.

(54) TAFFINDER, —, – Rotherham (Manufacturer and Designer).
An eight-day skeleton clock with lever escapement; design taken from Rotherham Cathedral.

(69) MAPPLE, D. D. – 17 Hulls Place, John's Row, St. Luke's.
Registered skeleton timepiece with improved lever escapement; improved clock winder.

(74) RIX, ISAAC – Conduit Street, Westbourne Terrace (Inventor).
Skeleton chronometer, slow motion beating only once in three seconds, the escapement so contrived as to allow the pendulum to vibrate two seconds every beat without touching anything; a perfectly dead escape.

(104) EDWARDS, JAMES – Stourbridge.

Large transparent skeleton timepiece made of a combination of brass and glass; the wheels consist of cut flint glass centres hooped with brass teeth rims, engraved glass dial plate and crystal cut pendulum ball. It goes for eight days.

A new skeleton (quarter-day) spring timepiece, made of flint glass centres hooped with brass teeth rims, having engraved glass dial plate and glass pendulum ball. It goes for three months and is kept in motion by a new clock propellor.

(105) EVANS, WILLIAM F. – Soho Street, Handsworth, Birmingham (Manufacturer).

Gothic skeleton clock. Detached lever escapement. Skeleton lever clock with representation of Sir Walter Scott monument in Edinburgh.

(117) PACE, J. – Bury St. Edmunds (Inventor and Designer, Manufacturer).

Skeleton clock which goes for three years; this period is obtained by the use of six springs, the united force of which is 250 pounds. They are enclosed in six barrels or boxes. Three are connected with chains to a fusee on the right hand and three to the one on the left. Pyramidical skeleton timepiece which goes for three months. The dial is placed at the bottom of the clock to show the motion of all the wheels with Graham dead-beat escapement and the hands move by a simple mechanism.

(129) SMITH & SONS, JOHN, LANCELOT, WILLIAM – St. John Square (Manufacturers).

Skeleton timepiece which goes twelve months with one winding and shows the seconds, minutes, with the day of the week and the month on one dial; skeleton quarter clock which chimes the quarters on eight bells and strikes on steel wire gong.

(131) YOUNG, —, – Knaresborough (Manufacturer).

Skeleton timepiece.

(128) SHEPHERD, CHARLES – 53 Leadenhall Street (Inventor and Patentee).

A skeleton magnetic striking clock showing how the number of blows to be struck is regulated.

The undermentioned are the remaining skeleton clock exhibitors who are included in the official handbook catalogue, but are not in the illustrated catalogue with those above.

(15) PIKE, H. C. – 9 Cumberland Row, Islington Green (Inventor and Manufacturer).

Skeleton clock striking going 400 days, it shows dead seconds by application of the chronometer escapement.

(82) TRITCHLER, J. – 402 Oxford Street, Westbourne Terrace (Inventor).
Skeleton clock with improved pendulum eight-day etc.

(107) FELTHAM, R. D. – King Street, St. Helier, Jersey.

Skeleton regulator to go 500 days having a metronome pendulum with detached escapement.

No mention of skeleton clocks is made in that part of the official catalogue referring to foreign horological exhibitors. However, in the horological section of the *Illustrated London News*, dated August 23, 1851, a review is given of the many foreign countries dealing exclusively in horological items.

There are only three instances where skeleton clocks are mentioned and these are all from France. The references are:

'V. Pecheloche: A thirty-five day skeleton clock, (note the unusual period); Pierret of Paris: Twelve small skeleton pendulum clocks,

M. Wagner, also exhibits on his stall, fronting the Nave, two examples of large skeleton works with compensation pendulums, and a chronometric apparatus to verify the law of gravity. This is placed next to the Nave and consists of a vertical cylinder made to rotate the clockwork: The cylinder is covered with paper on which lines are marked by means of a pen from which the necessary results are obtained.'

It was at this exhibition that Pierret of Paris sold 10,000 of his miniature skeleton timepieces, which included alarms (see page 69).

It was very disappointing to find that no illustrations of skeleton clocks, which might have given some clue to their design, style and origin were given in the illustrated catalogue. Some information can be analysed, however.

Every endeavour has been made to trace each exhibitor and his clock. Town councils, museums, historical and archaeological societies, librarians, and local research bodies in villages and various towns were enlisted to help, coupled with generous publicity from local newspapers. They have all been given the fullest particulars, dossiers, and original quotations from the official catalogue and other sources.

Great emphasis was placed on the importance of accurate documentation for the purpose of this book yet it became apparent that the outlook was bleak. Unfortunately many records were destroyed by enemy action. Other records were also lost or destroyed when establishments ceased to exist. More unfortunate were those cases where the introduction of modern methods or amalgamation meant that records simply went as waste paper.

It seems incredible that most of these manufacturers have faded into oblivion, leaving absolutely no trace of either their whereabouts or their exhibits. More strange is the fact that their own home towns had no knowledge of them or their clocks, not even the memory of a name of one who must have lived, worked and traded in their midst.

Some small successes were, nevertheless, achieved, and I succeeded in bringing to light some histories of skeleton-clock makers. Some are included in this chapter. Where, however, I have obtained accurate and fuller information the makers have been included in the chapter dealing with their work.

R. D. Feltham of King Street or Queen Street, St. Helier, Jersey, is an enigma. No record can be found of the five-hundred-day skeleton clocks attributed to him, and shown at the exhibition. During my research the Societe Jersaise, a society for archaeological, historical and local research, provided me with the only information available. This seems very meagre for such an important clock.

The following is an extract of a letter from the society:

'Unfortunately we cannot help, except to say that from our records R. Feltham was a silversmith and watchmaker at Queen Street, Jersey, in 1850. We would have expected to find some trace of his achievement but cannot.'

Of much interest was a printed pamphlet issued by the society, giving a list of Jersey names on grandfather clocks. Prefacing the forty-two listed names was the comment:

'The following names are either the clockmaker, the seller or the owner of the clock.'

R. D. Feltham does not even appear in this pamphlet, neither is he listed in any reference work.

The situation of John Pace, of Bury St. Edmunds, Suffolk, is similar. The exhibition catalogue mentions him as an inventor, designer and manufacturer, and refers to him as exhibiting a skeleton clock which goes for three years and a pyramidical skeleton timepiece which goes for three months. Exhaustive enquiries failed to produce any information about the clocks or a manufacturing concern.

The Bury St. Edmunds and West Suffolk Records Office provided, from their Poor Rate Assessments volumes for the parish of St. James, Bury St. Edmunds, the first mention of John Pace in Abbey Street in November 20, 1824, assessment, where No. 20 is assessed as a house. The name of John Pace is found in assessments up to, and including, October, 1868.

In another entry, of 1869, 'Pace' appears – the number of the house having been changed from 20 to 19 in April, 1867.

In a newspaper story dated July, 1853 headed 'A few Rhymes respecting Abbeygate Street, Bury St. Edmunds', the following passage occurs:

'A Silversmith is Mr. Pace
He makes new clocks, old ones, new face
Guards, Broaches, Pins and other things
Ah, "yes" and sells new wedding rings.'

John Pace's name appears in both Baillie's and Britten's reference books, yet persistent enquiries to find out where he was in business shed no further light.

An extremely brief reference of only seven words is given in the catalogue to James Lamb of Bicester, Oxon. It reads: 'skeleton clock to go for 400 days'. Enquiries have proved futile.

Lamb is recorded in *Clockmaking in Oxfordshire* by Dr. Beeson where he is described as being in Market Square from 1818–53 as a clock, watch, glass, china, and earthenware dealer. He was married at Bicester on March 14, 1818, to Anne Neale.

In 1854 directory confirms that James Lamb had a general store in Market Street and that he sold thirty-hour painted dial longcase clocks which he obtained from Birmingham and had inscribed with his own name.

Of William Harvey from Stirling, Scotland, described in the catalogue as an inventor and manufacturer, I have some engaging facts and anecdotes for which I am greatly indebted to the Town Clerk Depute of Stirling. The following quotations are taken from Harvey's obituary in the *Stirling Observer* dated Thursday, April 26, 1883.

'He was born in 1808 at St. Ninian's, which at the time was a village, but is now part of Stirling. William worked for his father, George Harvey, watchmaker in the town, and eventually succeeded to the business in King Street. An old apprentice, a Mr. Hunter, was assumed as partner, and the business carried on under the name of Harvey and

Hunter. In 1835 a daring robbery brought misfortune, Mr. Harvey losing several hundreds of pounds worth of goods. The sympathy felt for him found expression in the purchase of watches and jewellery, by which means his business was extended, and by his skill, his assiduous attention, and his upright dealing, he became the leading watchmaker in the town.

'Although not possessed of the artistic gift of his brother George (who was known to fame as Sir George Harvey, President of the Royal Scottish Academy), he had a talent of his own. He was of an inventive turn of mind, and constructed various machines, one of which is remembered as a successful instrument for the making of corks, and another as a reaping machine of ingenious make.'

Young of Knaresborough, Yorkshire, has only three words after his name in the catalogue: 'Manufacturer, skeleton clock'.

In a bid to amplify this scanty information enquiries were made to the Clerk of the Urban District Council of Knaresborough, but without success. No trace of Young could be found in this town, neither does his name appear in any reference work.

These comments apply equally to P. Robinson of Bishop Auckland, Co. Durham, whose quarter chiming skeleton clock purports to represent the entrance to the Bishop's Palace. The Urban District Council of Bishop Auckland state they have no details.

A. Taffinder, who hailed from Rotherham, is specified as a manufacturer and designer. His skeleton clock design is taken from Rotherham Cathedral. The County Borough Librarian provided the following references. The earliest mention of Abram Taffinder lists him as a watchmaker in 1841 at Westgate. In 1849 he was listed as a watchmaker in the Market Place. In 1862 in *Drake's Directory*, Abraham Taffinder was listed as a watchmaker and jeweller at 38 High Street. In the 1862 edition of *White's Directory* he appears as a watchmaker at 40 High Street. Taffinder is recorded as being at this address up to, and including, 1883.

The following extract is taken from the *Ivanhoe Review*, vol. 2, dated 1899.

'*An Exhibition Clock:* At the International Exhibition held in London in 1851, Mr. A. Taffinder of Rotherham, then a jeweller in the town, exhibited a beautiful clock of especial local interest. The clock itself, which is a remarkably fine specimen, was constructed by Mr. Taffinder. It is the case, however, that is the distinguishing feature. It consists of a well-designed model of Rotherham Church, in brass, which included all the salient features of that beautiful structure. All the castings were made by a Mr. Brammah, from moulds by a Mr. Mendon, both of whom were with Messrs. Yates & Haywood.'

It was certainly a very clever production for that time.

The exhibition catalogue describes Taffinder's clock as 'Rotherham Cathedral'. The church is Rotherham Parish Church, which was completed in the fifteenth century.

C. Thornloe of Lichfield, Staffs., designer and manufacturer, is shown to have exhibited a Gothic skeleton clock. This could not be traced.

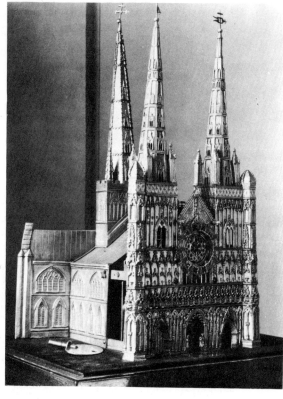

rear, allowing free movement of the travelling centre seconds hand. The clock has maintaining power.

The name of John Moore & Sons, Clerkenwell, London, is clearly stamped at the base of the frame, a common practice amongst the Clerkenwell clockmakers.

Fig. 11-3 shows the brass fretted dial which is silvered and upon which the Roman numerals are engraved. The movement stands upon a mahogany and ormolu base in the French style. The clock goes for eight days, is dated *circa* 1840, and is in Mr. Norman Langmaid's collection in Washington.

Moore was originally a partner in the well-known clock manufacturing firm Handley & Moore, also of Clerkenwell, and was subsequently part of the establishment of Moore & Sons. He is mentioned in Britten's reference book.

James Gowland was at 11 Leathersellers Buildings, London Wall, which is in the precincts of the City of London. He was a well-known chronometer maker and was born in 1880. Gowland is mentioned by Britten as in '1837 patenting (No. 7456) a device for communicating motion in a balance-spring through a balance-spring'. This was shown at the exhibition by being applied to a 'Patent Tourbillon Chronometer', its stud being advanced one degree on the tooth of a locking plate at each oscillation.

Charles Shepherd of 53 Leadenhall Street, which is also in the environs of the City of London, was an inventor and patentee. His electric skeleton clock must have caused a stir. It is described as a magnetic striking clock showing how the number of blows to be struck are regulated. An example of the electric skeleton clock can be seen in Figs. 1-31 and 1-32. It belongs to Mr. George Duncan, Norwich, Norfolk.

Again from Britten's book comes this information on Shepherd's work: 'In 1849 he patented (No. 12,567) an application for impelling clocks, and afterwards supplied an electric clock for driving the large dial just outside the gateway of Greenwich Observatory.'

Although I. Rix of Conduit Street, London, is said to have shown a specimen with chronometer escapement at the exhibition, his name does not appear in any works of reference, neither is he mentioned or named amongst the patentees of that period. As to the clock itself, we are again in a position of uncertainty and can offer no proof as to its present existence.

These remarks can also be applied to H. C. Pike of Islington Green, London, whose 400-day skeleton clock is recorded in the exhibition catalogue. The location of this highly important clock would have been of much horological interest. Apart from its year duration the clock had a striking mechanism and, with a chronometer escapement, was unique.

There is very little information other than that the city and county of Lichfield purchased a clock in the design of Lichfield Cathedral from the executors of the Thorneloe family. This is now displayed to the public in the county museum, and was shown at the Great Exhibition.

Although not a skeleton clock, it is a fine example of casting and display of emblem decoration. The motion work is, however, visible. It is quarter strike and goes for thirty-two days (Fig. 11-1).

Moore & Son of Clerkenwell Close, London, were well-known clock manufacturers. Their 1851 exhibit was a skeleton chiming clock which went for a month. Although the whereabouts of this clock cannot be traced, an example of their work was fortunately submitted to me.

As can be seen in Fig. 11-2 the pattern appears to be a complete breakaway from the usual fretted designs and could almost be described as a flower.

In spite of having only two trains, the clock chimes each quarter on eight bells, striking the hours on a deep ninth bell. The platform lever escapement fitted to the rear frame can be seen in Fig. 11-2, the platform itself conforming to the main design.

Of particular interest are the winding arbors, projecting from the rear frame. Having incorporated a centre seconds hand (the hand is missing in Fig. 11-3), Moore, a very experienced clockmaker, obviously planned to reverse these arbors, thus enabling the clock to be wound from the

11-2

11-3

Only two further names of exhibitors who showed skeleton clocks at the Great Exhibition remain – D. D. Mapple of St. Luke's, Clerkenwell, and Tritchler of Oxford Street, London.

Once more exhaustive enquiries have proved fruitless, and no mention can be found either of these individuals or of their exhibits. There is a possibility that these masterpieces are standing in a mansion or cottage whilst their owners remain oblivious of their importance.

Skeleton clocks at the Great Exhibition were referred to in a report in *The Illustrated News* of August 23, 1851.

'As already observed, the collection of British clocks and watches, forming part of Class 10, are worthy of close examination by every visitor. The arrangement of the collection has been made by a committee appointed by the Exhibition and certainly highly creditable to them. A peculiarity in this section of the Exhibition is that an intelligent person has been appointed to the special charge of the collection and, being himself a practical watch and clock maker, and very obliging, is not only able, but willing, to render every assistance to the enquiring multitude attracted by this costly horological display.'

A footnote to the Great Exhibition comes from the book *Clocks, Watches and Bells*, in which the author, Sir Edmund Beckett (late Lord Grimthorpe), the designer of the Great Westminster clock 'Big Ben', describes his design for a pin-wheel escapement. He adds that this design was incorporated in the large clock at King's Cross, from which the time of the Great Exhibition in Hyde Park was kept.

12-1 *Price list from Chance Bros. catalogue of 1859*

TARIFF No. 11.

CROWN GLASS SHADES, ROUND, OVAL, AND SQUARE,

For Covering Clocks, Vases, Lustres, Statuettes, and other Ornaments.

Our Shades are of a light colour, and very superior, in lustre and in quality, to those manufactured on the Continent. For orders for Stock, we recommend an assortment from the smallest to the largest size in current use (technically called, nests), in which case, a large number of Shades may be packed one within another in a small compass, and the cost of packing is very much reduced.

INCHES	PRICE. ROUND. s.	d.	OVAL. s.	d.	SQUARE. s.	d.
7	0	4	0	11	1	5
8	0	4	0	11	1	5
9	0	5	1	0	1	6
10	0	6	1	0	1	6
11	0	6	1	1	1	7
12	0	7	1	2	1	9
12½	0	7	1	2	1	10
13	0	7	1	3	2	0
13½	0	7	1	3	2	1
14	0	8	1	4	2	3
14½	0	8	1	4	2	4
15	0	9	1	6	2	5
15½	0	9	1	7	2	6
16	0	10	1	8	2	7
16½	0	10	1	9	2	8
17	0	11	1	10	2	9
17½	0	11	1	11	2	9
18	1	0	2	0	2	10
18½	1	0	2	1	2	10
19	1	2	2	2	3	0
19½	1	2	2	3	3	0
20	1	2	2	4	3	1
20½	1	3	2	5	3	1
21	1	3	2	6	3	2
21½	1	3	2	7	3	3
22	1	4	2	8	3	4
22½	1	4	2	9	3	5
23	1	4	2	10	3	6
23½	1	6	2	11	3	6
24	1	6	3	0	3	7
24½	1	6	3	0	3	8
25	1	7	3	1	3	9
25½	1	7	3	1	3	9
26	1	7	3	2	3	10
26½	1	8	3	2	3	10
27	1	8	3	4	3	11
27½	1	8	3	4	3	11
28	1	10	3	5	4	0
28½	1	10	3	5	4	0
29	1	10	3	6	4	1
29½	2	0	3	7	4	1
30	2	0	3	8	4	2
30½	2	0	3	9	4	2
31	2	1	3	10	4	4
31½	2	1	3	10	4	4
32	2	1	3	11	4	5

INCHES	PRICE. ROUND. s.	d.	OVAL. s.	d.	SQUARE. s.	d.
32½	2	2	3	11	4	5
33	2	2	4	0	4	6
33½	2	2	4	0	4	6
34	2	3	4	1	4	8
34½	2	3	4	2	4	8
35	2	3	4	3	4	9
35½	2	5	4	3	4	10
36	2	5	4	4	4	11
36½	2	5	4	4	5	0
37	2	6	4	5	5	1
37½	2	6	4	6	5	2
38	2	8	4	7	5	3
38½	2	8	4	8	5	4
39	2	10	4	9	5	5
39½	2	10	4	10	5	6
40	3	0	4	11	5	7
40½	3	0	5	0	5	8
41	3	1	5	1	5	9
41½	3	2	5	2	5	10
42	3	4	5	3	6	0
42½	3	6	5	4	6	3
43	3	7	5	5	6	6
43½	3	8	5	6	6	9
44	3	10	5	7	7	0
44½	4	0	5	8	7	3
45	4	2	5	9	7	6
45½	4	4	5	10	8	0
46	4	6	5	11	8	3
46½	4	8	6	0	8	6
47	4	10	6	2	8	9
47½	5	0	6	4	9	0
48	5	3	6	6	9	3
48½	5	6	6	9	9	6
49	5	9	7	0	10	0
49½	6	0	7	4	10	6
50	6	3	7	8	11	0
50½	6	6	8	4	11	6
51	6	9	8	8	12	0
51½	7	0	9	0	12	6
52	7	2	9	4	13	0
52½	7	4	9	8	13	6
53	7	6	10	0	14	0
53½	7	8	10	4	14	6
54	7	10	10	8	15	0
54½	8	1	11	0	15	6
55	8	4	11	4	16	0

INCHES	PRICE. ROUND. s.	d.	OVAL. s.	d.	SQUARE. s.	d.
55½	8	7	11	8	16	6
56	8	10	12	0	17	0
56½	9	2	12	6	17	6
57	9	6	13	0	18	0
57½	10	0	13	6	18	6
58	10	6	14	0	19	0
58½	11	0	14	6	19	6
59	11	6	15	0	20	0
59½	12	0	15	6	21	0
60	12	6	16	0	22	0
60½	13	0	16	6	23	0
61	13	6	17	0	24	0
61½	14	3	17	9	25	0
62	15	0	18	6	26	0
62½	15	6	19	3	27	0
63	16	0	20	0	28	0
63½	16	6	20	9	29	0
64	17	0	21	6	30	0
64½	17	6	22	3	31	0
65	18	0	23	0	32	0
65½	18	9	24	0	33	0
66	19	6	25	0	34	0
66½	20	0	26	0	35	0
67	21	0	27	0	36	0
67½	22	0	28	0	37	0
68	23	0	29	0	38	0
68½	23	6	30	0	39	0
69	24	0	31	0	40	0
69½	25	0	32	0	41	6
70	26	0	33	0	43	0
70½	27	0	34	0	44	6
71	28	0	35	0	46	0
71½	29	0	36	0	47	6
72	30	0	37	0	49	0
72½	31	0	38	0	50	6
73	32	0	39	0	52	0
73½	33	0	40	0	53	6
74	34	0	42	0	55	0
74½	35	0	44	0	56	6
75	36	0	45	0	58	0
75½	37	0	46	0	59	6
76	38	0	47	0	61	0
76½	39	0	48	0	62	6
77	40	0	49	0	64	0
77½	41	0	50	0	65	6
78	42	0	51	0	67	0

INCHES	PRICE. ROUND. s.	d.	OVAL. s.	d.	SQUARE. s.	d.
78½	43	0	52	0	68	6
79	44	0	53	0	70	0
79½	45	0	54	0	72	0
80	46	0	55	6	74	0
80½	47	0	57	0	76	0
81	48	0	59	0	78	0
81½	49	0	61	0	80	0
82	50	0	63	6	82	0
82½	51	0	66	0	84	6
83	52	0	68	6	86	0
83½	53	0	71	0	88	0
84	55	0	73	6	90	0
84½	57	6	76	0	92	0
85	60	0	78	6	94	0
85½	62	6	81	0	96	0
86	65	0	83	6	98	0
86½	67	6	86	0	100	0
87	70	0	88	6	102	0
87½	72	6	91	0	104	0
88	75	0	94	0	106	0
88½	77	6	97	0	109	0
89	80	0	100	0	112	0
89½	83	0	103	0	115	0
90	86	0	106	0	118	0
90½	89	0	109	0	121	0
91	92	0	112	0	124	0
91½	95	0	115	0	127	0
92	98	0	118	0	130	0
92½	101	0	121	0	133	0
93	104	0	124	0	136	0
93½	107	0	127	0	139	0
94	110	0	130	0	142	0
94½	113	0	133	0	145	0
95	116	0	136	0	148	0
95½	119	0	139	0	151	0
96	122	0	142	0	154	0
96½	125	0	145	0	157	0
97	128	0	148	0	160	0
97½	131	0	151	0	163	0
98	134	0	154	0	166	0
98½	137	0	157	0	169	0
99	140	0	160	0	172	0
99½	143	0	163	0	175	0
100	146	0	166	0	178	0
100½	149	0	169	0	181	0
101	152	0	172	0	184	0

INCHES	PRICE. ROUND. s.	d.	OVAL. s.	d.	SQUARE. s.	d.
101½	155	0	175	0	187	0
102	158	0	178	0	190	0
102½	161	0	181	0	193	0
103	164	0	184	0	196	0
103½	167	0	187	0	199	0
104	170	0	190	0	202	0
104½	173	0	193	0	205	0
105	176	0	196	0	208	0
105½	179	0	199	0	211	0
106	182	0	202	0	214	0
106½	185	0	205	0	217	6
107	188	0	208	0	221	0
107½	191	0	211	0	224	6
108	194	0	214	0	228	0
108½	197	0	217	6	231	6
109	200	0	221	0	235	0
109½	203	6	224	6	238	6
110	207	0	228	0	242	0
110½	210	6	231	6	245	6
111	214	0	235	0	249	0
111½	217	6	238	6	252	6
112	221	0	242	0	256	0
112½	224	6	245	6	259	6
113	228	0	249	0	263	0
113½	231	6	252	6	266	6
114	235	0	256	0	270	0
114½	238	6	259	6	274	0
115	242	0	263	0	278	0
115½	245	6	266	6	282	0
116	249	0	270	0	286	0
116½	252	6	274	0	290	0
117	256	0	278	0	294	0
117½	259	6	282	0	298	0
118	263	0	286	0	302	0
118½	266	6	290	0	306	0
119	270	0	294	0	310	0
119½	274	0	298	0	315	0
120	278	0	302	0	320	0
120½	282	0	306	0	325	0
121	286	0	310	0	330	0
121½	290	0	315	0	335	0
122	294	0	320	0	340	0
122½	298	0	325	0	345	0
123	302	0	330	0	350	0
123½	306	0	335	0	355	0
124	310	0	340	0	360	0

All Shades containing more than 124 inches, 5s. per half inch extra.

EXPLANATION OF THE SCALE.

The total number of inches in a shade is to be found by the following calculation:—

ROUND SHADES—Once the height added to three times the diameter. *Example*—12 height, 6 diameter, make 30 inches. Price 2s. 0d.

OVAL & SQUARE SHADES—Once the height, twice the length, once the breadth. *Example*—12 height, 8 length, 5 breadth, make 33 inches. Price 4s. & 4s.6d. respectively.

N.B.—However low a Shade may be ordered, the height is in no case charged less than the diameter or length.

N.B.—All Oval and Square Shades made to pattern or special sizes, will be charged double the above prices, unless at least two of the same size be ordered at one time.

NOT ACCOUNTABLE FOR BREAKAGE

CHAPTER 12

SHADES: CLOCK REPAIR

Glass shades and bases

The birth of the skeleton clock in England stimulated allied professions by its use of marble and glass. In consequence, the prolific output of the skeleton clock covered by a glass shade, contributed in no small measure to the glass blowing industry, which was already coping with covers for stuffed birds, waxed fruit, flowers, statuettes, etc. It was the era of the glass shade.

The clockmakers' dream became the clockwinders' nightmare. In those days the clock repairer had a large clientele to whom he was under contract solely for the purpose of winding the clocks in their homes. It was an integral part of his business. In the weekly chore of the clock-winder, lifting off and on the glass shades must have caused many anxious moments and one can clearly imagine many an apprentice or improver receiving a salutory cuff for cracking, or breaking a shade. Shades, however, were easy to buy in those days. In at least one shade, holes had been drilled to correspond with the winding squares, the holes being reinforced by brass collets from a dial plate. The winding key arm was extended to reach the movement. One cannot but admire such patient ingenuity.

Before their manufacture in this country, such shades were imported from France and Belgium. In the early part of the nineteenth century, Chance Brothers, of Spon Lane, Birmingham, introduced the manufacture of sheet glass. Subsequently, in the 1830s, they took up the manufacture of glass shades, importing and employing French and Belgian glass-blowers. An off-shoot of the company W. E. Chance & Co., of Oldbury, also began in this sphere at Nailsea, to help out with production, but eventually closed down in 1873, leaving the main production to the parent firm at Birmingham.

In the early days a glass shade was blown in a mould. The mould was then probably made of wood, but later, after further developments, the material became cast iron. Shades were annealed in a kiln and the bottoms cut off and finally ground flat with an abrasive. Chance Brothers' catalogue of 1856, under the heading TARIFF 11 (see Fig. 12-1), indicates that they could supply over 200 sizes, ranging from fourpence for a 7-inch shade up to 360 shillings for a 124-inch shade. It was their boast that their shades were of a light colour and very superior in lustre and quality to those produced on the Continent.

Incidentally Chance Brothers supplied the whole of the sheet glass to glaze the Crystal Palace of the Great Exhibition, which was held in Hyde Park in the year 1851. Over one million square feet of glass was

The St. Helen's Crown Sheet & Plate Glass Company, of St. Helen's, Lancashire, was a rival but friendly firm, which also produced glass shades on a considerable scale. The price lists of the same period from both companies (Fig. 12-3) show an exact similarity. They tally word for word, price for price.

The St. Helen's Glass Company are the world famous Pilkington Brothers Ltd., who also retain their old and original site at St. Helen's.

An amusing advertisement printed in the hand catalogue of the Great Exhibition reads as follows:

> 'Glass shades for the covering and preservation of Clocks, Statuettes, Waxflowers, Alabaster, and other articles of vertu.
>
> Claudet & Houghton, of Holborn.
>
> Having considerably reduced their prices of *Glass Shades* they may be appropriated advantageously, not only as above but also in protecting goods exposed to sale from dust, and the impurities of the atmosphere.
>
> From our Wholesale and Retail Glass Shade Warehouse.'

Marble and wood bases predominated in the mounting of all movements, the bulk being oval. Some individual specimens may be seen in solid brass, which was cast. For the earliest models a deep base was favoured, usually in rosewood, with slight brass inlay in varied design, a hangover from the Regency period. Mother-of-pearl decoration was another inclusion but was short-lived. Many bases were, however, square or rectangular, the finer quality having a foundation of a frosted brass gilt base, often with an engraved cross-banded or scalloped edge. This could be as much as an $\frac{1}{8}$-inch thick, and was, in turn, sunk flush on top of the wooden base and screwed down.

Unlike the decoration of Continental models, applied motifs and scrolled or ornate fancy feet were never typical of English clock bases. In the minute number that do carry this form of embellishment it is, in my opinion, an added feature. For the cheaper clock, considerable numbers of bases were made of pinewood and were painted a gloss black. A channelled groove was provided to enable the glass shade to sink in, and underneath the base four bun feet were nailed.

White marble was often used. Bases of this material had a marble step laid on top, over which the glass shade lapped, to prevent it sliding. Expensive coloured marble is rare as an English skeleton clock base.

The majority of skeleton clock movements rest on four cup-like cast brass feet of matching design in different patterns, some two inches or so in height. As the clock gets larger and more massive, six, eight, and even

used. They are still a great force in the glass-making industry of the 1960s, and continue their business from their original address at Spon Lane, Birmingham.

The records of Chance Brothers also provide the first written evidence that chenille was used at the base of the shade to keep out the dust. This was one of their sidelines, and they requisitioned it from other firms (as the record shows the charges coming from a firm named 'Smith' and the prices in turn charged by Chance Brothers), according to an entry written on June 18, 1861 (see Fig. 12-2, where it is interesting to note the spelling of 'Chenille' and its correction). As an accessory, chenille could be purchased in various colours. For perfect fit, it was cut and sewn at the ends to go over about two-thirds of the shade and then rolled to the base, chenille being very elastic.

These oddments could be purchased even in the tool and material shops of the day in Clerkenwell and Soho.

ST. HELENS CROWN, SHEET & PLATE GLASS CO.'S
PRICES OF
CROWN GLASS SHADES,—ROUND, OVAL, AND SQUARE,
AT THEIR WAREHOUSE, 10, SNOW HILL, BIRMINGHAM.

Inches.	Round.	Oval.	Square.	Inches.	Round.	Oval.	Square.	Inches.	Round.	Oval.	Square.	Inches.	Round.	Oval.	Square.	Inches.	Round.	Oval.	Square.
	s. d.	s. d.	s. d.		s. d.	s. d.	s. d.		s. d.	s. d.	s. d.		s. d.	s. d.	s. d.		s. d.	s. d.	s. d.

(Detailed price table — extensive numeric entries by size in inches for Round, Oval, and Square shades)

EXPLANATION OF THE SCALE.
The total number of inches in a Shade is to be found by the following calculation:—
ROUND SHADES.—Once the height added to three times the diameter. *Example*—12 height, 6 diameter, make 30 inches.—Price 2s.
OVAL AND SQUARE SHADES.—Once the height, twice the length, once the breadth. *Example*—12 height, 8 length, 5 breadth, make 37inches.
Price 4s. and 4s. 6d. respectively.

N.B.—However low a Shade may be ordered, the height is in no case charged less than the diameter or length.

N.B.—All Oval and Square Shades made to pattern, or special sizes, will be charged double the above prices, unless two of the same size be ordered at one time.

Packages charged, but allowed for if returned in good condition, free of carriage, within one month.

June 1st, 1857.   NOT ACCOUNTABLE FOR BREAKAGE.

---

ten cup-like feet are used (Fig. 2-21). At the base of the front and rear frames it is customary to find steel screwed rods fitted. A brass cup is placed through each rod and the rods holding the cups, in turn, are pushed through the top of the base. The whole assembly is kept together by nuts or thumbscrews on to the end of the rods protruding through the base.

It is worth recording that, especially on timepieces, only two rods were employed, one in the corner of the front frame, the other on the opposite corner of the back frame, the two remaining corners having only an inch or so, or half rod, solely for the purpose of keeping the existing two cups in position. Thus the complete movement is held only on two nuts. When one draws comparisons with clocks produced on the Continent, the sameness of English clock bases borders on the brink of monotony.

The marble bases stimulated Continental production by enabling manufacturers there to enter the fray with their 'tombstone efforts'. These were marble cased clocks which were not only cheap and shoddy, but had a mausoleum-like and sombre appearance. Nevertheless they became a challenge to the English skeleton clock industry, so strong was the new cult for marble. Even the Americans cashed in with pseudo-marble clock cases, which, in fact, were cast iron, the marbling being painted by specialists who had for years been marbling shop fronts.

Sometimes in deep bases crude attempts have been made to incorporate a small two or more tune musical movement with key and comb mechanism. Clocks with this adaptation cannot be classified as musical clocks. The musical movement is placed under the base, and an arm or lever is taken up through the base to the minute-wheel of the clock, which sets off the musical sequence as arranged. In some instances, common to French clocks of all descriptions, the musical sequence can be played at will by pulling a cord which winds the musical movement, and on release allows the movement to play itself out. Often this conversion destroys a fine base.

Imported musical movements were made in various sizes and were also accommodated in bracket clocks.

In spite of intensive enquiries, it has been impossible to trace any marble masons, however long established, who fashioned bases.

All the early-established marble specialists have been unable to trace in their records any specific reference to marble bases being made for skeleton clocks, and, where marble bases are mentioned, they are not referred to as being *clock* bases. Some of these firms originated as early as 1821, and several others were established in the 1830s, among those who entered business in the years up to 1870.

Probably it was thought to be more economical to import the marble clock bases ready made. The majority of expensive marble bases were already being imported from France, since that country had almost a monopoly, having produced exquisite examples in this medium for many years.

There is reason, therefore, to suppose that they shipped to this country, in bulk, less expensive clock bases which met the needs of the clockmaker manufacturing the cheaper variety of skeleton clock.

Repairing skeleton clocks
All mainsprings must be let down before any dismantling is carried out.

It is of great importance when taking down a movement, and where pillar screws are incorporated for both front and rear frames, *always* to remove the front screws first.

Should the pillars on the rear frame need to be taken apart (as they must when the clock is being cleaned), it is advisable to remove them one at a time, marking both the seating and base end of the pillar. This will ensure that pillars are returned to their corresponding seatings.

Fortunately a great many of the larger and later chiming skeleton clocks were provided by the manufacturers with identification, by placing spot marks on both the seating and pillar. This practice is also found on high-quality regulators and good class movements where pillar work is screwed at both ends.

More often than not, all the trains will be found fully wound and, in consequence, pallets have to be removed and the movement allowed to run down. The same procedure applies to the striking mechanisms after the gathering pallets have been removed.

Clockmakers often tend to forget that a much easier method can be resorted to. On many fusee great wheels a small hole can be discerned which has been drilled centrally between the teeth. This has a specific purpose, for, if a key (preferably a crank key) is applied to the fusee square and held tightly, the point of stiff blue steel wire (pivot steel) may be inserted into this hole. This in turn will release the hidden click from the fusee ratchet, thus enabling one to unwind the mainspring. It is as simple as that. It will also be found that considerable time has been saved, particularly when letting down the striking and chiming trains.

No special comment is called for with regard to the repairs. One must be specially mindful, however, to use great care in handling the frame. As in all clocks, depths, endshake, worn pivots, and large holes must be checked and dealt with. This includes the striking and chiming trains. Instructions have already been given in practical textbooks, such as *Practical Clock Repairing*, by Donald de Carle (N.A.G. Press Ltd.).

With skeleton clocks, the bushing of holes should be carried out with infinite care. Holes should be broached open very carefully and slowly; the broach must not be forced.

The bush to be introduced, whether ready-made, or of your own turning, must not be too *large*. Otherwise, when the bush is struck home, the frame will expand or spread, and probably crack. All too often soft solder has been used wrongly to keep the parts together. Unfortunately one finds bushes in the weakest parts of the frame. When inserting the bush, a dead-flat surface is desirable, and a hard one at that. At all times the bush must be inserted from the inside of both front and rear frames.

Sometimes attempts have been made to close the holes by using a punch. This is disastrous to the frame and must not be encouraged, besides being wrong in practice.

Clean always by hand. Make no attempt whatsoever to clean or polish the frame with electric polishers with high revolutions, as this could end in disaster, both for the frame and yourself. It may be irksome to clean by hand and progress will be slow, but it is better that, than having a buckled frame. Skeleton clocks are slow items to clean and repair, and cannot be rushed.

When all repairs have been effected, clean and polish the frame crossings before the rest. They will show up better against the dirty face of the frame and you are not likely to miss any.

It will probably be found that the frame, if held between the knees, offers less resistance whereas, fixed in a vice or clamp, it is held rigid and could therefore buckle or break. For the best results, use chamois-leather strips dipped in any good metal polish, which can then be pulled to and fro through the crossings by both hands. When the faces of the frames have been cleaned and buffed, wash off (benzine or petrol is suitable), then, when dry, brush off in the ordinary manner with French chalk.

The frames and pillars should then be lacquered in the colour chosen. One important fact must be remembered here. All holes must first be well pegged out, and care taken that the lacquer does not run into any of the holes. When the lacquer is perfectly dry, the holes should be pegged out once more. Bells should be treated with colourless lacquer.

All too frequently there are signs of a lazy approach to cleaning frame crossings. They are either scraped or filed, and, in many cases, look rather tawdry. Where no lacquer is available, soak the frames in methylated spirits for about ten minutes, wipe dry, and again chalk and brush off. Methylated spirits will prevent tarnishing for a much longer period than any other cleansing liquid.

For a complete finish, all screws, steel collets, clicks (if they be steel), ratchets, and steel emblems should be blued. If expense is no object, the frames could be frost gilt, as many were in their heyday. This treatment will greatly add to the appearance.

One last, but most important, reminder. If at any time the frame is found to be cracked or broken, the offending part must be brazed, and in no circumstances must soft solder be used.

Repairs to French skeleton clocks are not likely to produce any undue hazards. Their frames are straight-forward, but still need care in handling. When executing repairs, the work may be carried through the usual routine stage.

Although a number of winding ratchet wheels have cocks to hold them in place, the majority of ratchet wheels on French clocks – up to 1820 or so – are held to the arbor squares by a simple pin. The pin, more often than not, is usually left straight. This is a dangerous practice where going barrels are concerned, for, when in the act of winding, the pin can and does easily drop out and cause damage both to the owner and the clock.

The steel pin should be fashioned round the square in 'S' formation to ensure complete safety.

SIMPLE GLOSSARY
FOR NON-HOROLOGICAL READERS

Anchor (or recoil) escapement – clock control with escape wheel and anchor-shaped pallet arm.

Arbor – axle.

Balance – oscillating wheel or bar which, with a hairspring, controls timekeeping through the escapement.

Barrel – rotating drum from which a clock is driven by weight or spring.

Barrel cap – disc in end of barrel with mainspring in it.

Beat – tick.

Beat adjustment – means of making ticks even.

Bob – weight of a pendulum.

Bridge – support bar fixed at both ends.

Cannon pinion – toothed wheel with tube which carries minute hand.

Chapter ring – circle bearing the 'chapters' marking the hour.

Chronometer escapement – accurate detent escapement.

Clickwork – ratchet wheel and pawl.

Cock – support bar fixed at one end.

Collet – loose or fixed washer.

Compensated – made to reduce timekeeping errors through temperature changes.

Contrate wheel – band wheel with the teeth on one side.

Count wheel (locking plate) – notched wheel that controls striking.

Coup perdu – pin-wheel escapement that misses every other beat.

Crossing – spoke of a wheel.

Crown wheel – band wheel with pointed teeth like a king's crown.

Crutch – lever which connects clock to pendulum via a pin or fork.

Dead beat – moving in jumps without recoiling.

Depthing – the degree to which toothed wheels engage.

Detached escapement – one in which the pendulum or balance is disconnected from the clock most of the time.

Detent – a lever that holds up some action.

Detent escapement – one employing a detent.

Draw – geometrical arrangement to prevent an escapement from tripping.

Duplex escapement – one with two escape-wheels or one wheel with two sets of teeth.

Escape-wheel – wheel that is released in small jumps to control the rate of a clock.

Escapement – escape-wheel and its releasing device, which is controlled by the balance or pendulum.

Finial – decoration at the top.

Fly – rotating fan to reduce speed of striking, musical trains, etc.

Fusee – trumpet-shaped pulley to give even output from mainspring.

Going – timekeeping part.

Going barrel – barrel with spring in it that drives in the same direction as winding.

Grande sonnerie – striking the last hour before chiming each quarter.

Grasshopper escapement – one with pallet arms that move like grasshoppers.

Gravity escapement – constant force escapement in which the pendulum is impulsed by the force of gravity.

Great wheel – main wheel of a fusee clock.

Gridiron pendulum – compensated pendulum with a row of pendulum rods.

Hairspring (balance spring) – fine coiled spring used with oscillating balance.

Half dead beat – less accurate dead beat escapement.

Huygens endless chain – continuous chain for clock weight which provides maintaining power.

Impulse – the tiny push which keeps a pendulum or balance swinging.

Impulse pin (or pallet) – the part through which impulse is given.

Lantern pinion – a wheel like a squirrel case.

Leaf – tooth of a pinion.

Lever escapement – one which impulses a balance wheel by means of a lever action.

Lifting piece – lever which sets off striking, etc.

Mainspring – coiled spring for driving a clock.

Maintaining power – means of keeping the clock going while it is being wound.

Mercurial gilding – method of gilding before electro-plate was invented.

Mercurial pendulum – compensated pendulum with jar of mercury for a bob.

Minute wheel – gear wheel that turns once an hour.

Moon hand – style with a pierced circle near the point.

Motion work – gearing between minute and hour hands.

Ormolu – French term for mercurial gilding applied only to bronze or brass.

Orrery – working model of part of the solar system.

Pallet – part of an escapement that holds up the teeth of the escape-wheel.

Pin-wheel escapement – one with a series of pins round the escape-wheel.

Pinion – small, wide gear wheel.

Platform escapement – one mounted on a separate platform attached to the clock.

Potence – cock used as a lower bearing.

Pull repeat – means of sounding the last hour or quarter by pulling a cord.

Rack – toothed arm that controls striking.

Rating nut – nut on bottom of pendulum to adjust timekeeping.

Regulator dial – dial with hands that are not concentric.

Remontoire – means of providing controlled driving force for accurate timekeeping.

Rise and fall – regulator for easily altering pendulum length from the top to change timekeeping.

Seconds pendulum – one that swings from side to side in a second.

Set beat – adjustment to make ticks equally spaced.

Set up – pre-tensioning of the main spring when used with a fusee.

Slave clock – separate dial operated from a master clock.

Snail – snail-shaped cam.

Staff – axle of the balance wheel.

Star wheel and jumper – arrangement to give positive positions to a calendar, for example.

Stop work – means of preventing over or under winding.

Sun hand – hand with sunburst decoration.

Sundial time – solar time, which varies, unlike clock time.

Suspension – means of hanging the pendulum, e.g. ribbon, steel, silk thread, and knife edge.

Tic-tac (or drum) escapement – small form of anchor escapement.

Timing screws – screws on the rim of a balance to alter timekeeping.

Train – series of engaging gears.

Verge and crown wheel escapement – early type with an axle holding two pallets (the verge).

Wheel – thin toothed wheel which drives a pinion.

INDEX

Aeits of Tongres, J. B. 115
Airy, G. B. (Astronomer Royal) 22
Alarm 70
Allen, Adrian (Assistant Archivist) 20
Allix, Charles R. P. 2, 26, 107, 126
Anchor (recoil) escapement 8, 16, 21, 23, 24, 32, 33, 41, 66, 70, 71, 81, 111, 132
Anderson, Dr. Joe E. 24
Anniversary clock 150
Antiquarian Horology 107
Arkwright, Sir Richard 99

Bagshaw, D. 100
Baillie, G. H. 45, 60, 80, 88, 93, 95, 136
Bain principle 22
Banham Ltd., Keith 141
Banking pin 48
Barraud 103
Barrel work and appendages 7, 21, 25, 27, 38, 41, 47, 48, 50, 51, 62, 72, 73, 75, 76, 78, 85, 88, 91, 104, 105, 106, 112, 119, 142, 154
Barwise 14
Base 163
Beat adjustment 7, 11, 32, 91, 124
Beckett, Sir Edmund 161
Bell of Winchester, Geoffrey H. 91
Bell, Maynard E. 141, 151, 156
Bells, 27, 67
    glass 86
    hemispherical 9, 67
    Kent treble 121
    peals (crests) of 29, 47, 115, 117, 118, 121
    standard 9
    true 9, 141
Belper, Lord 100, 141
Berthoud, Ferdinand 3, 109
Bertrand, Charles 79
Bezel 36, 41, 53, 68, 77, 78, 80, 81, 85, 87, 129
Biddell, G. A. 17
Birmingham Museum, City of 2, 37
Black, Thos. 146
Blandford, Malcolm 154
Blaylock, John 35
Bobinet Ltd. 141
Bolt and shutter 11
Boulton & Watt 37
Brazing 165
Breguet 144, 145, 151
British Horological Institute 93, 134
British Telegraph & Manufacturing Co. Ltd. 22
Britten, F. J. 41, 124, 160
Brocklehurst, Aubrey 141, 154
Brocot escapement 4, 70

Brutom, Eric M. 1, 2
Buckingham Palace 9, 140
Buhl or boulle 53

Carlton House 136
Carnelian or cornelian 4
Cast figures 13, 38, 66
Castle Museum, York 8
Central Telegraph Office 22
Chamberlain, The Rt. Hon. Joseph 41
Chance Bros. 162, 163
Chance, Sir Hugh 2
Chenille 163
Chiming 6, 7, 29, 35, 53, 120, 121, 157, 160
Chinn, E. W. 23, 24
Chronometer escapement 8, 11, 15, 16, 23, 38, 133, 157, 160
Claudet & Houghton 163
Clerkenwell 159
Clickwork 9, 85, 88, 95, 119, 126
Clockmaking in Oxfordshire 159
Clock Repairing (N. A. G. Press) 165
Clocks & Watches, An Historical Bibliography 80, 93, 95
Cock 9, 14, 85, 89, 94, 118, 127
Coe, J. W. 31
Coldwell, George Henry 119, 120, 121
Collet or washer 11, 12, 24, 41, 47, 48
Condliff, James 45, 47, 48, 50, 51
Congreve, Sir William 36, 136, 137, 139, 140
Conover Jr., E. R. 141
Conservatoire National des Arts et Metiers 79, 81, 85
Constant force (remontoire) escapement 66, 78, 82, 83, 89, 91, 93, 95, 127, 145, 157
Cooke's principle 22
Counterpoise 81, 97, 107
Count wheel (or locking plate) 7, 15, 67, 70, 73, 81, 85, 86, 91, 94, 117, 126, 128
Coup perdu escapement 18
Court of Versailles 64
Cox, James 107
Crutch 38, 62, 68
Cups (or movement feet) 17, 21, 24, 32, 41, 163, 164

Daily Chronicle (Leeds ed.), *The* 119
Darwin, Dr. 99
Deadbeat and half deadbeat escapement 7, 8, 16, 18, 23, 24, 25, 26, 27, 28, 35, 62, 70, 72, 73, 80, 91, 95, 158
Debaufre escapement 85, 113
De Carle, Donald 165
Denison, E. B. (Lord Grimthorpe) 63

Derby Mercury 99
Detached escapement 8, 28, 29, 31, 37, 38, 39, 136, 137
Detent escapement 146, 147
Dent 148
Detouche of Paris, C. 87
Dial: Arabic 21, 48, 75, 79, 95, 105, 128
    Calendar (or date) 21, 66, 75, 80, 88, 89, 91, 95, 106, 108, 111, 112, 116, 117, 154, 156
    Chapter ring of 14, 15, 16, 17, 24, 26, 31, 32, 33, 48, 70, 73, 75, 140
    feet 23, 48
    Gilt 26, 68
    Glass 41, 43, 97
    Lunar (or moon) 68, 73, 75, 108, 120
    Minute ring of 28
    One-piece 18, 111
    Painted 48
    Pilot 120
    Planetary 113
    Regulator 28, 32, 152
    Roman 24, 25, 35, 41, 48, 68, 70, 71, 73, 77, 80, 86, 98, 105, 116, 129
    Rotating (circles or rings) 28, 100, 106
    Seconds 15, 18, 28
    Silvered 15, 25, 26, 73
    Skeleton 3, 107
    Subsidiary 9, 20, 47, 66, 68, 73, 75, 79, 107, 113, 116
    Tidal 120
    Twenty-four hour 48, 112
    World wide 113
Directoire period 67, 70, 75, 81
Dobson of Leeds 122
Duke of Orleans 87
Duplex escapement 8, 98, 112
Dutertre, Jean Baptiste 88
Dwherrihouse, Ogston & Bell 17, 18

Earnshaw, Thomas 31, 139
Earnshaw free-spring balance 146
Eccentric ring 70, 125
Eccles, Frederick Henry 15
Eccles, George 14
Edgeworth, Maria 99
Edwards, James 41, 43, 45
Electric clock 21
Ellicott temperature-compensation 86
Emblem 12, 13
Empire period 67, 70, 81
Endstone (piece) 11
Epicyclic gearing 99, 100
Equation 80, 108
Escutcheon plate 17, 47, 48, 85
Evans, Miss Phyllis B. 2, 37
Evans, Mrs. Sarah 37

Evans, William Frederick 17, 37, 40, 41, 158

Fan (or fly) 7, 11, 32, 94, 95, 120
Feltham, R. D. 20
Ferguson F. R. S., James 120
Four-hundred day clock 150
Fournier, Bernard Gavin 65
Frame 11, 12, 15
    Fretted 4, 47
    Rafter 4, 18, 19, 32, 33, 35, 50, 64, 66, 73, 75, 78, 81, 88, 109, 119, 127, 140
    Scroll 4, 7, 14, 17, 21, 23, 24, 28, 35, 41, 43, 48, 60
Frodsham & Co., Charles 117, 139
Fulcrum 80
Fusee 7, 14, 21, 27, 140, 149, 158, 165
    cap 24, 41
    chain 12, 27, 38, 41, 110, 112
    clickwork 165
    engine 53, 60
    Great wheel of 16, 29, 31, 32, 33, 41, 47, 64
    roller 12, 27

Gears (gearing) 11, 28, 115
Gong 47, 48, 67, 115
    block 9, 154
    rod 9
    standard 27
    wire 7, 9, 32, 35
Gothic cathedral clock 6, 53, 60, 157
    Grant, Capt. W. A. 100
Grasshopper escapement 8, 31
Gravity escapement 6, 8
Great Exhibition of 1851 4, 20, 37, 41, 43, 70, 124, 157, 158, 159, 162, 163
Great Wheel at Earl's Court 6
Greenwich Mean Time 2, 103, 113, 120
Guiness, Mrs. Lee 7
Gut lines 12, 104

Hagans Clock Manor Museum 119
Hairspring: Conical 8
    Flat 11
    Helical 8, 11, 25, 35, 47, 50, 140, 146, 147
    stud 11
Halifax moon 100, 103
Hammer (striking) 7, 8, 9, 17, 23, 24, 25, 26, 27, 32, 36, 50, 67, 86, 91, 107, 118, 120
Harlow, Samuel Boulton 60
Harrington Patent Carillon Tubes 7, 15, 41, 120
Harris, The Rt. Hon. Lord 110
Harrison, James 31

Harrison, John 31
Hastings Municipal Library 2
Hawkins Collection 32
Haycock & Co. 57, 60, 61
Helix gearing 8, 61, 62
Higgins, Rev. H. H. 14
Hills of Sudbury 141, 152
Hirst, Albert 119
Houghton, John 37, 41
Hugenin 87
Huygens endless drive 97, 141

Ilbert, Courtenay A. 6, 93, 99
Illustrated London News 21, 51, 158, 161
Impulse pin (or pallet) 11, 31, 38, 47, 85, 128
Index, Regulating 38, 79, 115
Ionides Collection 83

Johnsson, J. A. 141
Jutson, Benjamin 137

Langmaid, N. 141
Lattimore, Dr. C. R. 141
Lee, Ronald A. 141
Lengelle, Monsieur A. 2
Lepaute, Jean Andre 3, 66, 80, 96, 99
Lepine, Jean Antoine 3, 79
Le Roy Pierre 3, 95, 99
Lever escapement 11, 22, 36, 38, 48, 50, 115, 157
Lichfield Cathedral 53
Lifting arm (or piece) 7, 9, 12, 16, 45, 70, 85, 114, 126, 127
Litherland, Peter 45
Liverpool Museum, City of 2, 14, 47
London District Telegraph Co. 22
Lorraine et Bar, Duc de 93
Louis XIV 64
Lyre clock 113, 115, 148

MacDowell, Charles 62, 63
Magnac, Colonel 53
Mainspring 7, 41, 62, 94, 110, 132
Maintaining power 11, 25, 28, 31, 32, 35, 36, 38, 47, 50, 81, 98, 140, 160
Mercure de France 96
Merlin, Jas. 107
Monogram frame 148
Month clock 14, 24, 64, 153
Moore, Lieut.-Colonel 134
Moore & Son 160
Morbier (or Comtoise) clock 71, 124
Motion work 12, 22, 24, 27, 41, 48, 62, 64, 78, 88, 95, 98, 109
Moxon, John 136, 137, 140
Mudge & Dutton 21

Musical clocks 9, 67, 115, 116, 117, 118, 119, 120, 121, 164

Old Clocks, Watches and their Makers 41, 124, 160
Old Clockmakers of Yorkshire 124
One-at-the-hour (strike) 7, 8, 17, 23, 24, 36, 53
Ormolu 5, 69, 77, 80, 88, 113, 127
Outside escapement (U.S. term) 4

Pace, John 14, 20
Pallet 8, 11, 18, 25, 31, 32, 35, 36, 47, 48, 50, 72, 77, 78, 85, 89, 96, 118, 124, 127, 134, 136, 165
Parker, Benjamin 20, 112
Pearsons & Sons of Romford 110
Pendule d'Officer 68, 88
Pendule Français 83, 92
Pendulum 67, 68, 71, 88, 89, 100
    Conical 155
    Ellicott 86
    Harrison 68, 72, 73, 75, 80, 86, 94, 109, 125, 144, 150
    Lepaute 80
    Torison 150
Pendulum bob: Brass 68, 103
    Cylindrical 14, 24, 29, 31
    Intaglio (glass) 68
    Lenticular (or lens) 14, 41, 68, 80, 81, 85
    Mercurial 7, 14, 26, 31, 132
Pendulum rod: Brass 14, 68
    Gridiron 68, 72, 73, 75, 80, 86, 94, 109, 125, 144, 150
    Steel 14, 85, 98
    Wood 14, 24, 123
Pendulum suspension: Knife edge (and double) 8, 68, 80, 83, 85, 87, 88, 91, 94, 97, 127
    Pivot 68, 73
    Ribbon steel 8, 14, 62, 68, 75, 81, 109
    Silk 8, 70, 77, 129
Perpetual calendar 72, 103, 120
Perpetual motion 92
Phillippe Egalite, Duc d'Orleans 87
Pickering, Dr. 124
Pierret, Victor Athenase 70, 158
Pike, H. C. 20, 42
Pilkington Bros 163
Pillar 9, 12, 17, 24, 32, 35, 41, 48, 62, 71, 110, 140, 165
Pinion 8, 12, 20, 28, 61, 62, 64, 78, 83, 88, 95, 100, 103, 104, 106, 107, 110, 111, 119, 122, 123, 124, 126, 134
Pinwheel escapement 8, 16, 18, 19, 66, 72, 73, 75, 77, 78, 79, 80, 81, 83, 87, 88, 89, 107, 109, 149

Planus, Gerry 22
Platform escapement 8, 11, 16, 19, 47, 132, 160
Plinth 17, 18, 25, 26
Potence 35, 36
Practical Clock Repairing 165
Prince, J. 124

Quarter chime (or strike) 7, 8, 48, 67, 94, 129, 142, 154
Quarter day 43

Rack 7, 9, 12, 15, 16, 67, 71, 120, 124
Ratchet 7, 14, 18, 23, 31, 47, 67, 70, 75, 81, 85, 98, 119, 128
Rating nut (or timing screw) 8, 14, 31, 35, 47
Reeve, C. B. 35, 124, 125
Regulator 32, 122, 152, 158
Remontoire 66, 78, 82, 83, 89, 91, 93, 95, 127, 145, 157
Repeating mechanism 9, 70, 116, 129
Repertory of Arts 137
Revolving escapement 151
Rippin of Spalding 28
Rise and fall 14, 41, 45, 70, 106
Rolling ball drive 155
Roskell (or Roskill) 45, 147
Royal Greenwich Observatory 21, 160
Royal Mint 37
Royal Pavilion, Brighton 6
Royal Scottish Museum 121
Royal Society 100

Sarcelly Cross 9
Sarton, Hubert 93, 95
Sauniers Treatise 87
Savage escapement 147
Saw teeth 67

Scheblin, Robert N. 141
Scissors clock 88
Scoreby, William 47
Scott's Memorial Clock 6, 17, 37, 158
Shade, Glass 22, 36, 162, 163
Shepherd's patent electric clock 21, 160
Simmons & Co. 32
Smith & Sons, John 20, 21, 23, 27, 32, 51, 53, 57, 142
Snail (striking) 8, 9, 12, 35, 50, 115
Societe Jeraise 158
Soho 163
Spirit level 11, 35
St. Helen's Crown Sheet & Plate Glass Company 163
Stainless steel frame 153
Stevens, John 141, 153
Stopwork 9, 11, 91
Strutt, Jedediah 99
Strutt F.R.S., William 99, 141

Tardy of Paris 83, 92
Tarleton, William 45
Terry, Silas 131
Thouverez of Paris, Louis 87, 88
Three-month clock 6, 53, 73, 75, 126
Three train 26, 27, 35
Thumbscrew 11, 14, 73, 75, 80, 87, 91
Tic-tac (or drum escapement) 64, 66
Ting tang 7, 86, 92, 94, 118, 126
Tourbillion escapement 151
Trade mark 4, 60
Transparent clock 67, 81, 158

Verge escapement 106
Verneuil of Dyon 75
Villemsen et Cie, N. S. 135
Viner & Co. 18
Visible escapement 4
Vulliamy, Benjamin Louis 125, 136, 137

Watchmakers and Clockmakers of the World 45, 60, 88, 136
Weight 15, 67, 78, 80, 81, 83, 91, 92, 95, 121
West Suffolk Records Office 159
Wheatstone principle 22
Wheel cutting machine 53, 60
Wheel arbor 11, 41
Wheel balance 8, 19, 31, 35, 47, 78, 79, 85, 127, 140
Wheel: Calendar 67
    Centre 41, 62, 78, 103, 124
    Contrate 91
    Crown 106
    Escape 4, 21, 25, 35, 38, 41, 47, 48, 50, 62, 77, 78, 83, 85, 89, 96, 98, 100, 104, 118, 123, 124
    Flint glass 41, 43, 158
    Great 62, 76, 78, 83, 88, 91, 103, 109, 118
    Hour 100
    Intermediate 91, 109, 111, 115, 127
    Internal 121, 122, 123
    Minute (or idle) 8, 28, 45, 83, 127, 164
    Papier mâché 134, 135
    Planet 99
    Sun 100
    Third 41, 62, 77, 91, 109, 124
    Verge 31, 105
    Whitehurst, F.R.S., John 60
Williams, Lieut.-Colonel 70
Wild, J. M. 141
Wray & Son 19
Wright, Jacobo 104
Wyke, John 45

Year (or more) clock 20, 21, 53, 64, 109, 110, 111, 112, 113, 157, 158, 159
York Minster 6, 9, 32